Ten Divided by Five Is Not Five

Using Multiplication to Make Division Easy

Susan Greenwald, M.A. Ed.

LP **LONGEVITY PUBLISHING, LLC**
Englewood, Colorado • www.LongevityPublishing.com

This book has been a labor of love
for students of all ages,
and will continue to be beneficial
for as long as children need to memorize math facts.

To Madison Olivia and Morgan Harper, with love.

Ten Divided by Five Is Not Five:
Using Multiplication to Make Division Easy
LP 500

Copyright © 2014 by Susan Greenwald
All rights reserved.
Printed in U.S.A. by Sheridan Books on acid-free paper.

Longevity Publishing LLC
Englewood, Colorado
www.LongevityPublishing.com
ISBN 13: 978-0-9777323-3-3
10 9 8 7 6 5 4 3 2

First printing 2014

Edited by: Susan Hindman, Wordwise Editing
Design by: DBS, Inc.
Cover Design by: Lee Lewis Walsh, Words Plus Design

Table of Contents

Introduction

Ten Divided by Five Is Not Five: Using Multiplication to Make Division Easy (LP 500) is a supplementary workbook designed to introduce and teach division facts based on a student's knowledge of multiplication facts.

Fluency of math facts is essential for success and proficiency in computation skills, and for solving real-life math problems.

The six sections of workbook pages help students of any age who need to become fluent with and memorize division facts. For this reason, the workbook pages were intentionally not designated for a particular grade level.

The 60 reproducible practice pages will appeal to:
- Beginners
- Elementary school children needing instruction, practice, or review of the division facts
- Children in remedial programs
- Children in accelerated programs who need to memorize division facts
- Children with math disabilities
- Older students or adults who struggle because they just never memorized these math facts

---

If you use *Five Times Five Is Not Ten: Make Multiplication Easy* (LP 400), you will find that the sequence in which the multiplication facts is introduced there is the same order as the multiplication and related division facts in this book. You can use the two workbooks together!

★ Classroom teachers, ★ homeschooling educators, ★ parents, ★ resource room teachers, and ★ tutors will appreciate that:

- Multiplication facts are reviewed in each of the six sections, so students see how multiplication facts (such as 3×5 and 5×3) are related to division facts (such as $15 \div 3$ and $15 \div 5$).
- Once introduced, the division facts are used throughout the book.
- Each section includes a page of **Word Problems**.
- Lessons can be easily individualized for different learning abilities.
- Cleanly designed reproducible pages offer a lot of written practice.
- Math assignments can be completed with confidence, and students will experience success.

How to Use This Book, a **Guide to Introducing Division, Pre- and Post-Assessments, Answers,** a **Record-Keeping Checklist,** and a **Certificate of Mastery** are provided.

Enjoy teaching math!
Susan R. Greenwald, M.A. Ed.

How to Use This Book

Before we ask children to memorize any division facts, they need to:

- Know how to count to at least 81.
- Demonstrate understanding of multiplication. (**6×8**: Show **6×8** as **6** *groups of* **8**, and be able to count out the **48** items.)
- Demonstrate understanding of division. (**48÷6**: Show **48÷6** as **48** items divided into **6** *groups with* **8** *in each group*, or as **8** *groups of* **6** *items*.)
- Be able to tell a word problem related to the fact being taught. (**48÷6**: There are **48** crayons. If **6** crayons are put into each bag, how many bags will be needed? Or, if there are **6** bags, how many crayons will be in each bag?)

Excluding facts with Zero, there are **81 division facts**. As you introduce the pages, you may want to refer to the **Guide to Introducing Division** on page vii.

Division can be expressed three different ways. In this workbook, division is presented in the first two ways:

$$16 \div 8 = 2 \qquad 8\overline{)16}^{\,2} \qquad 16 \,/\, 8 = 2$$

For the example above:

> **16** is the **dividend**.
> **8** is the **divisor**.
> **2** is the **quotient**.
> **2 and 8** are the **factors**.

If the divisor does not fit evenly into the dividend, the piece left over is called the remainder.

9÷4=2 r 1

The remainder is 1. This practice book *does not* include division problems with remainders.

Some Rules in Division

All even numbers are divisible by 2.
A Number divided by 1 = that Number.   **8÷1=8**   (**8×1=8**)
A Number divided by itself = 1.   **8÷8=1**   (**1×8=8**)
Zero divided by a Number = 0.   **0÷8=0**   (**0×8=0**)

NOTE: A Number ÷ Zero is not possible. Example: 8÷0=

Ask, "**0×?=8**" There is no answer. Nothing multiplied by **0=8**!

Where to Begin

> **For use with beginners or students who need to learn all the division facts:**
> Start with step 3 in the **Guide to Introducing Division** on page vii.

> **For use with individuals, or when working with small groups of students who have some knowledge of division facts:**
> Begin with step 1 in the **Guide to Introducing Division**.

> **For use by a classroom teacher with students who have some knowledge of division facts:**
> A. Begin with the **Pre-Assessment** on page 59 to get a baseline of which facts are known. Encourage your students to answer *only the ones they know without counting* and to skip over and leave the others blank. ***Known*** facts are those division facts that are answered quickly and correctly. Students should not count to get an answer.
> B. Record those *known* division facts on the **Math Facts Baseline Recorder** on page 61 and follow the rest of step 2 on the next page.
> C. **Tip**: Use a clean copy of the **Pre-Assessment** page to keep a tally of students who did not know particular facts. For example, if 16 students did not know the answer to $72 \div 8$, then mark 16 on top of that fact. If only two students did not know or had recorded a wrong answer for $20 \div 4$, mark 2 on top of that fact.

Types of Workbook Pages

There are six types of workbook pages in this practice book. Not all students will need to complete each page in its entirety. Set the pace according to your class and, if possible, divide the class into smaller groups, to provide some individualization and to differentiate.

A. **Multiplication**: The first workbook page in each section has a set of multiplication facts for review and practice. These facts are used to teach the related division facts in that section.

B. **Missing Factors**: These pages have multiplication facts that require students to fill in the unknown factor to make the equation true. (**4 × _?_ = 12   _?_ × 2 = 10**)

C. **Word Problems**: Students will use division, multiplication, addition, and/or subtraction to solve word problems.

D. **Division**: The related division facts are practiced two ways. Once the related division facts are introduced, those facts will be reviewed throughout the book.

E. **Mixed Division and Multiplication**: Each section has a page of division and multiplication facts practiced together. Call attention to the mix of multiplication and division signs on this practice page.

F. **Cumulative Practice**: Students will be checked on the newly learned division facts and most of the others that have been taught from previous sections. Optional: Use these pages to time students for speed.

Ten Divided by Five Is Not Five: Using Multiplication to Make Division Easy

Guide to Introducing Division

1. Use a set of division flash cards to determine the **Baseline** of which division facts are known. (Or, see the previous page on how to use the **Pre-Assessment**.)

2. **Known** facts are those division facts that are answered quickly and correctly. Students should not count to get an answer.

   Record those known facts on the **Math Facts Baseline Recorder** provided on page 61. Then transfer the information to the **Record-Keeping Checklist** on page 62. After marking the known facts, unmarked spaces allow you to see easily which facts need to be learned. The workbook is designed to be used in sequence, so start with the first **section** in which there are unmarked spaces.

3. Ask students to draw a picture or an array or to use counters, to show what a particular multiplication fact means.

   A. Have students solve a word problem by drawing a picture or an array or by using counters. Example: There are **4 tables**, and each table has **3 computers** on it. How many computers are there in all?

   Students need to show **4 groups of 3** and count to show the answer is **12** computers.

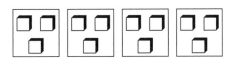   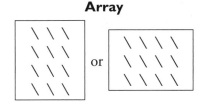

Array

   Have students write a math sentence. **4×3=12**

   B. Change the word problem to **3 tables** with **4 computers** on each table, and follow the directions in A above.

   Multiplication is commutative, meaning the order of the factors does not matter.

   If 3×4 is known, then 4×3 is also known.

   For those students who have not yet memorized **multiplication** facts, *Five Times Five Is Not Ten: Make Multiplication Easy* (LP 400) helps students learn **multiplication** facts. Pages 1-24 of that book should be completed before beginning this division workbook.

4. Provide students with plastic sandwich bags and crayons or other small counting items. *Before we ask them to memorize the facts,* students need to show understanding of division. Some examples:

   A. If you have **8 crayons** and **place 2 into each plastic bag**, how many bags will you need?

   Ask your students to **_divide_** or put 2 crayons into each bag.   **8÷2=4**
   Students can also draw a picture to show **8÷2**.

B. Division is the same as repeated subtraction.

Students can solve problems with repeated subtraction. Ask, "How many 2s can you subtract from 8?" The number 2 is subtracted four times.

$$8-2=6; \quad 6-2=4; \quad 4-2=2; \quad 2-2=0$$

NOTE: The same division problem, **8÷2**, can be worded differently. "If you have **8 crayons** and **place them evenly into 2 bags**, how many crayons will go into each bag?"

The question is different, and the picture is different, but the number answer is the same.

After the word math is solved, say, "8 *divided* by 2 is 4."

C. Start again with 8 crayons. Ask, "If you have **8 crayons** and **place 4 into each plastic bag**, how many bags will you need?" Follow the steps A and B above.

5. Review the relationship between multiplication and division.

$$2 \times 4 = 8 \text{ and } 4 \times 2 = 8 \text{ with } 8 \div 4 = 2 \text{ and } 8 \div 2 = 4$$

For **8÷2=____** or **8÷____=2**   Ask **2× _?_ =8**

For **8÷4=____** or **8÷____=4**   Ask **4× _?_ =8**

4 bags of 2 crayons = 8 crayons. **4×2=8**

2 bags of 4 crayons = 8 crayons. **2×4=8**

6. Optional: When beginning a section, use 3″ by 5″ blank index cards to make a division fact card for each fact taught in that section. (Cards for previously known facts can also be made for practice.)

Teachers and parents can incorporate practice of division fact cards into their daily program.

7. Work a few problems together and then allow students to complete the page. Teachers and parents can assign the practice pages for class work and/or homework.

Tip: If students have difficulty with the multiplication pages, check if they have learned the listed multiplication facts for that section.

8. As new facts are mastered, be sure to mark the **Record-Keeping Checklist** on page 62. Seeing those filled-in spaces will give students a feeling of accomplishment!

9. Meaningful, real-life word problems help children see reasons for learning new math skills and assist in the **transfer of those skills to solving real-life math problems**. Students should have some instruction with word math vocabulary. Encourage students to make up their own division word problems.

10. A Certificate for Mastery of Division Math Facts is provided on page 63.

Name _____

Multiply.

A.	$\begin{array}{r}2\\ \times\,5\\\hline\end{array}$	$\begin{array}{r}8\\ \times\,1\\\hline\end{array}$	$\begin{array}{r}2\\ \times\,7\\\hline\end{array}$	$\begin{array}{r}1\\ \times\,1\\\hline\end{array}$	$\begin{array}{r}9\\ \times\,2\\\hline\end{array}$	$\begin{array}{r}2\\ \times\,2\\\hline\end{array}$

A.
$\begin{array}{r}2\\ \times\,5\\\hline\end{array}$
$\begin{array}{r}8\\ \times\,1\\\hline\end{array}$
$\begin{array}{r}2\\ \times\,7\\\hline\end{array}$
$\begin{array}{r}1\\ \times\,1\\\hline\end{array}$
$\begin{array}{r}9\\ \times\,2\\\hline\end{array}$
$\begin{array}{r}2\\ \times\,2\\\hline\end{array}$
$\begin{array}{r}8\\ \times\,7\\\hline\end{array}$

B.
$\begin{array}{r}5\\ \times\,1\\\hline\end{array}$
$\begin{array}{r}1\\ \times\,2\\\hline\end{array}$
$\begin{array}{r}0\\ \times\,8\\\hline\end{array}$
$\begin{array}{r}2\\ \times\,3\\\hline\end{array}$
$\begin{array}{r}2\\ \times\,4\\\hline\end{array}$
$\begin{array}{r}8\\ \times\,2\\\hline\end{array}$
$\begin{array}{r}1\\ \times\,9\\\hline\end{array}$

C.
$\begin{array}{r}3\\ \times\,2\\\hline\end{array}$
$\begin{array}{r}2\\ \times\,6\\\hline\end{array}$
$\begin{array}{r}3\\ \times\,3\\\hline\end{array}$
$\begin{array}{r}2\\ \times\,9\\\hline\end{array}$
$\begin{array}{r}1\\ \times\,3\\\hline\end{array}$
$\begin{array}{r}1\\ \times\,4\\\hline\end{array}$
$\begin{array}{r}4\\ \times\,2\\\hline\end{array}$

D.
$\begin{array}{r}5\\ \times\,2\\\hline\end{array}$
$\begin{array}{r}2\\ \times\,8\\\hline\end{array}$
$\begin{array}{r}6\\ \times\,2\\\hline\end{array}$
$\begin{array}{r}7\\ \times\,1\\\hline\end{array}$
$\begin{array}{r}7\\ \times\,8\\\hline\end{array}$
$\begin{array}{r}7\\ \times\,2\\\hline\end{array}$
$\begin{array}{r}1\\ \times\,6\\\hline\end{array}$

E.
$\begin{array}{r}8\\ \times\,7\\\hline\end{array}$
$\begin{array}{r}4\\ \times\,1\\\hline\end{array}$
$\begin{array}{r}2\\ \times\,5\\\hline\end{array}$
$\begin{array}{r}9\\ \times\,1\\\hline\end{array}$
$\begin{array}{r}1\\ \times\,8\\\hline\end{array}$
$\begin{array}{r}6\\ \times\,2\\\hline\end{array}$
$\begin{array}{r}1\\ \times\,5\\\hline\end{array}$

F.
$\begin{array}{r}6\\ \times\,1\\\hline\end{array}$
$\begin{array}{r}7\\ \times\,8\\\hline\end{array}$
$\begin{array}{r}4\\ \times\,2\\\hline\end{array}$
$\begin{array}{r}2\\ \times\,9\\\hline\end{array}$
$\begin{array}{r}1\\ \times\,7\\\hline\end{array}$
$\begin{array}{r}2\\ \times\,7\\\hline\end{array}$
$\begin{array}{r}2\\ \times\,8\\\hline\end{array}$

G.
$\begin{array}{r}9\\ \times\,2\\\hline\end{array}$
$\begin{array}{r}5\\ \times\,2\\\hline\end{array}$
$\begin{array}{r}2\\ \times\,1\\\hline\end{array}$
$\begin{array}{r}1\\ \times\,0\\\hline\end{array}$
$\begin{array}{r}8\\ \times\,7\\\hline\end{array}$
$\begin{array}{r}3\\ \times\,3\\\hline\end{array}$
$\begin{array}{r}3\\ \times\,1\\\hline\end{array}$

H.
$\begin{array}{r}2\\ \times\,2\\\hline\end{array}$
$\begin{array}{r}7\\ \times\,1\\\hline\end{array}$
$\begin{array}{r}8\\ \times\,2\\\hline\end{array}$
$\begin{array}{r}2\\ \times\,6\\\hline\end{array}$
$\begin{array}{r}2\\ \times\,4\\\hline\end{array}$
$\begin{array}{r}1\\ \times\,6\\\hline\end{array}$
$\begin{array}{r}2\\ \times\,3\\\hline\end{array}$

Ten Divided by Five Is Not Five: Using Multiplication to Make Division Easy

Name _____

Find the missing factor.

A. $5 \times \underline{\hspace{1cm}} = 10$ $8 \times \underline{\hspace{1cm}} = 56$ $1 \times \underline{\hspace{1cm}} = 8$ $2 \times \underline{\hspace{1cm}} = 2$

B. $2 \times \underline{\hspace{1cm}} = 14$ $\underline{\hspace{1cm}} \times 6 = 6$ $\underline{\hspace{1cm}} \times 1 = 7$ $1 \times \underline{\hspace{1cm}} = 4$

C. $2 \times \underline{\hspace{1cm}} = 4$ $3 \times \underline{\hspace{1cm}} = 9$ $9 \times \underline{\hspace{1cm}} = 18$ $\underline{\hspace{1cm}} \times 1 = 3$

D. $1 \times \underline{\hspace{1cm}} = 7$ $2 \times \underline{\hspace{1cm}} = 18$ $\underline{\hspace{1cm}} \times 2 = 16$ $2 \times \underline{\hspace{1cm}} = 6$

E. $9 \times \underline{\hspace{1cm}} = 9$ $5 \times \underline{\hspace{1cm}} = 0$ $7 \times \underline{\hspace{1cm}} = 56$ $\underline{\hspace{1cm}} \times 2 = 10$

F. $\underline{\hspace{1cm}} \times 3 = 6$ $1 \times \underline{\hspace{1cm}} = 5$ $4 \times \underline{\hspace{1cm}} = 8$ $2 \times \underline{\hspace{1cm}} = 12$

G. $1 \times \underline{\hspace{1cm}} = 6$ $8 \times \underline{\hspace{1cm}} = 8$ $3 \times \underline{\hspace{1cm}} = 3$ $1 \times \underline{\hspace{1cm}} = 2$

H. $8 \times \underline{\hspace{1cm}} = 16$ $\underline{\hspace{1cm}} \times 2 = 8$ $1 \times \underline{\hspace{1cm}} = 9$ $5 \times \underline{\hspace{1cm}} = 5$

I. $\underline{\hspace{1cm}} \times 6 = 12$ $1 \times \underline{\hspace{1cm}} = 1$ $4 \times \underline{\hspace{1cm}} = 4$ $\underline{\hspace{1cm}} \times 7 = 14$

Ten Divided by Five Is Not Five: Using Multiplication to Make Division Easy

Name _____

Word Problems and Division

Show what the division problem means. Write a number sentence and solve.

A. Morgan's dance class had 14 girls in it. The dance teacher asked the girls to get into groups of 2. How many groups of 2 were there?

Answer: _____

B. There were 9 third-grade boys in the computer club. The teacher said, "I want one boy at each table." How many tables were needed?

Answer: _____

C. Mr. Green has 56 new orange trees to plant in his orchard. He decided to plant 7 trees in each row. How many rows of trees will he need?

Answer: _____

D. Lily, Rae, and Erin earned $9 selling cookies. Lily divided the money equally between them. How much money did they each get?

Answer: _____

E. David had 16 wooden cars. He wanted to put 8 cars on each shelf. How many shelves will he need?

Answer: _____

F. On Monday, 4 boys and 8 girls signed up to be on the chess team. Each team has 2 players. Will there be enough children to form 8 teams?

Answer: _____

Name _____

Divide.

A. $56 \div 8 =$ ___ $12 \div$ ___ $= 6$ $4 \div 1 =$ ___ $18 \div 9 =$ ___ $9 \div 3 =$ ___

B. $7 \div 7 =$ ___ $8 \div 4 =$ ___ $10 \div 2 =$ ___ $0 \div 4 =$ ___ $4 \div$ ___ $= 2$

C. $16 \div 2 =$ ___ $2 \div 2 =$ ___ $1 \div 1 =$ ___ $10 \div 5 =$ ___ $8 \div 8 =$ ___

D. $9 \div$ ___ $= 9$ $7 \div 1 =$ ___ $5 \div 5 =$ ___ $6 \div$ ___ $= 2$ $6 \div 1 =$ ___

E. $9 \div 3 =$ ___ $0 \div 5 =$ ___ $16 \div 2 =$ ___ $5 \div 1 =$ ___ $56 \div 7 =$ ___

F. $18 \div 9 =$ ___ $8 \div 2 =$ ___ $3 \div 1 =$ ___ $4 \div 4 =$ ___ $8 \div 1 =$ ___

G. $10 \div 5 =$ ___ $56 \div 8 =$ ___ $9 \div$ ___ $= 3$ $14 \div 2 =$ ___ $0 \div 2 =$ ___

H. $16 \div$ ___ $= 8$ $3 \div 3 =$ ___ $2 \div 1 =$ ___ $18 \div 2 =$ ___ $14 \div$ ___ $= 2$

I. $8 \div 4 =$ ___ $10 \div 2 =$ ___ $6 \div 6 =$ ___ $12 \div 6 =$ ___ $16 \div 2 =$ ___

J. $6 \div 3 =$ ___ $56 \div$ ___ $= 7$ $14 \div 7 =$ ___ $6 \div 2 =$ ___ $9 \div 9 =$ ___

Name _____

Divide.

A. $1\overline{)8}$ $2\overline{)8}$ $2\overline{)10}$ $7\overline{)56}$ $8\overline{)16}$ $5\overline{)10}$

B. $6\overline{)6}$ $3\overline{)9}$ $2\overline{)6}$ $8\overline{)8}$ $9\overline{)18}$ $4\overline{)8}$

C. $2\overline{)16}$ $7\overline{)14}$ $1\overline{)5}$ $7\overline{)7}$ $8\overline{)56}$ $6\overline{)12}$

D. $3\overline{)0}$ $2\overline{)4}$ $2\overline{)12}$ $1\overline{)2}$ $3\overline{)3}$ $2\overline{)18}$

E. $2\overline{)14}$ $3\overline{)6}$ $1\overline{)4}$ $7\overline{)56}$ $1\overline{)7}$ $2\overline{)2}$

F. $8\overline{)16}$ $3\overline{)9}$ $5\overline{)10}$ $1\overline{)6}$ $4\overline{)4}$ $1\overline{)3}$

G. $1\overline{)9}$ $2\overline{)6}$ $9\overline{)9}$ $2\overline{)12}$ $2\overline{)18}$ $1\overline{)1}$

H. $8\overline{)56}$ $3\overline{)6}$ $7\overline{)0}$ $2\overline{)8}$ $5\overline{)5}$ $7\overline{)14}$

Ten Divided by Five Is Not Five: Using Multiplication to Make Division Easy

Name _____

Divide and multiply.

A. $12 \div 2 =$ ___ $56 \div 8 =$ ___ $2 \times 3 =$ ___ $6 \div 3 =$ ___ $16 \div 8 =$ ___

B. $5 \div 5 =$ ___ $2 \times 6 =$ ___ $18 \div 2 =$ ___ $4 \div 1 =$ ___ $1 \times 2 =$ ___

C. $3 \times 3 =$ ___ $10 \div 5 =$ ___ $1 \times 8 =$ ___ $0 \div 9 =$ ___ $6 \div 2 =$ ___

D. $8 \div 2 =$ ___ $4 \times 1 =$ ___ $9 \div 1 =$ ___ $16 \div 2 =$ ___ $8 \times 7 =$ ___

E. $5 \times 1 =$ ___ $7 \div 7 =$ ___ $8 \div 4 =$ ___ $12 \div 6 =$ ___ $3 \div 1 =$ ___

F. $10 \div 2 =$ ___ $5 \times 2 =$ ___ $56 \div 7 =$ ___ $8 \times 2 =$ ___ $14 \div 2 =$ ___

G. $56 \div 8 =$ ___ $18 \div 9 =$ ___ $7 \times 8 =$ ___ $2 \div 2 =$ ___ $7 \div 1 =$ ___

H. $4 \times 2 =$ ___ $4 \div 2 =$ ___ $2 \times 7 =$ ___ $2 \times 9 =$ ___ $9 \div 9 =$ ___

I. $10 \div 5 =$ ___ $18 \div 2 =$ ___ $1 \div 1 =$ ___ $14 \div 7 =$ ___ $6 \times 0 =$ ___

J. $9 \div 3 =$ ___ $3 \div 3 =$ ___ $6 \div 1 =$ ___ $1 \times 9 =$ ___ $8 \div 1 =$ ___

Ten Divided by Five Is Not Five: Using Multiplication to Make Division Easy

Name _____

Multiply.

A.	4 × 3	8 × 7	6 × 2	2 × 5	3 × 3	6 × 3	1 × 7

A. 4   8   6   2   3   6   1
   × 3 × 7 × 2 × 5 × 3 × 3 × 7

B. 5   5   2   3   4   2   4
   × 5 × 2 × 3 × 4 × 4 × 9 × 2

C. 7   9   3   7   3   9   8
   × 8 × 9 × 1 × 2 × 6 × 1 × 2

D. 4   1   6   1   4   5   3
   × 4 × 6 × 3 × 8 × 3 × 5 × 6

E. 9   2   7   2   1   1   3
   × 9 × 7 × 8 × 4 × 1 × 3 × 4

F. 5   0   9   3   1   2   8
   × 1 × 3 × 2 × 6 × 4 × 6 × 7

G. 1   3   2   6   3   9   6
   × 9 × 2 × 8 × 1 × 4 × 9 × 3

H. 4   1   5   4   2   7   4
   × 3 × 2 × 5 × 4 × 2 × 1 × 1

Ten Divided by Five Is Not Five: Using Multiplication to Make Division Easy   **7**

Name _____

Find the missing factor.

A. $9 \times \underline{\quad} = 18$ $9 \times \underline{\quad} = 81$ $4 \times \underline{\quad} = 12$ $2 \times \underline{\quad} = 6$

B. $2 \times \underline{\quad} = 14$ $\underline{\quad} \times 4 = 16$ $\underline{\quad} \times 6 = 18$ $5 \times \underline{\quad} = 5$

C. $5 \times \underline{\quad} = 25$ $1 \times \underline{\quad} = 8$ $2 \times \underline{\quad} = 4$ $\underline{\quad} \times 2 = 12$

D. $3 \times \underline{\quad} = 12$ $7 \times \underline{\quad} = 14$ $\underline{\quad} \times 9 = 9$ $3 \times \underline{\quad} = 18$

E. $5 \times \underline{\quad} = 10$ $1 \times \underline{\quad} = 1$ $8 \times \underline{\quad} = 16$ $\underline{\quad} \times 1 = 6$

F. $\underline{\quad} \times 8 = 56$ $4 \times \underline{\quad} = 16$ $6 \times \underline{\quad} = 12$ $2 \times \underline{\quad} = 8$

G. $6 \times \underline{\quad} = 18$ $2 \times \underline{\quad} = 18$ $4 \times \underline{\quad} = 8$ $3 \times \underline{\quad} = 3$

H. $2 \times \underline{\quad} = 16$ $\underline{\quad} \times 9 = 81$ $3 \times \underline{\quad} = 6$ $2 \times \underline{\quad} = 10$

I. $\underline{\quad} \times 3 = 12$ $4 \times \underline{\quad} = 0$ $3 \times \underline{\quad} = 18$ $\underline{\quad} \times 5 = 25$

   Ten Divided by Five Is Not Five: Using Multiplication to Make Division Easy

Name _____

Solve the problems.

A. There were 12 pencils in a box. Jamie's teacher asked her to put
    3 pencils on each table. How many tables had pencils?

Answer: _____
_____

B. Lisa's school had 8 third-grade classrooms, 7 fourth-grade
    classrooms, and 3 fifth-grade classrooms. How many third-
    and fourth-grade classrooms were in the school?

Answer: _____
_____

C. Matthew's dad gave him $2 for each day he did chores around the
    house. Matthew did chores every Monday, Thursday, and Sunday
    for 4 weeks. How much did he earn in all?

Answer: _____
_____

D. There are 12 large desks and 13 smaller desks in Dan's
    classroom. If the classroom has 5 even rows of desks, how
    many desks are in each row?

Answer: _____
_____

E. Adam has 9 toy cars and 2 toy trucks in each box. If he had 81 toy
    cars, how many boxes did he have? How many toy trucks did he
    have?

Answer: _____
_____

F. Sarah and her friends earned $14 selling lemonade and $7 selling
    cupcakes. They paid Sarah's mom back $3 for supplies and
    shared the rest of the money. If each girl got $6, how many girls
    were there in all?

Answer: _____

Name _____

Divide.

A.   25÷5=___   6÷___=3   12÷3=___   12÷4=___   18÷2=___

B.   4÷4=___   16÷4=___   12÷2=___   9÷3=___   10÷___=2

C.   18÷6=___   81÷9=___   8÷1=___   18÷9=___   4÷2=___

D.   56÷___=8   2÷1=___   18÷3=___   7÷___=7   8÷4=___

E.   16÷8=___   1÷1=___   56÷7=___   25÷5=___   16÷4=___

F.   12÷4=___   18÷6=___   10÷2=___   14÷2=___   8÷2=___

G.   0÷6=___   8÷8=___   12÷___=3   5÷1=___   81÷9=___

H.   16÷___=4   25÷5=___   9÷9=___   18÷3=___   3÷___=1

I.   4÷1=___   0÷8=___   12÷6=___   6÷6=___   12÷4=___

J.   5÷5=___   14÷___=7   6÷2=___   18÷6=___   16÷2=___

Ten Divided by Five Is Not Five: Using Multiplication to Make Division Easy

Name _____

Divide.

A. $2\overline{)10}$ $5\overline{)25}$ $2\overline{)14}$ $4\overline{)16}$ $9\overline{)18}$ $3\overline{)12}$

B. $1\overline{)6}$ $3\overline{)18}$ $9\overline{)9}$ $4\overline{)12}$ $9\overline{)81}$ $7\overline{)56}$

C. $2\overline{)4}$ $6\overline{)18}$ $2\overline{)2}$ $2\overline{)16}$ $6\overline{)6}$ $3\overline{)9}$

D. $6\overline{)12}$ $2\overline{)8}$ $7\overline{)14}$ $3\overline{)18}$ $3\overline{)12}$ $6\overline{)18}$

E. $8\overline{)16}$ $9\overline{)0}$ $5\overline{)25}$ $2\overline{)18}$ $1\overline{)7}$ $3\overline{)6}$

F. $8\overline{)8}$ $9\overline{)81}$ $2\overline{)6}$ $8\overline{)56}$ $4\overline{)16}$ $2\overline{)12}$

G. $6\overline{)18}$ $1\overline{)5}$ $4\overline{)8}$ $1\overline{)3}$ $4\overline{)12}$ $3\overline{)18}$

H. $5\overline{)25}$ $8\overline{)0}$ $4\overline{)16}$ $3\overline{)12}$ $9\overline{)81}$ $5\overline{)10}$

    Ten Divided by Five Is Not Five: Using Multiplication to Make Division Easy

Name _____

Divide and multiply.

A. $81 \div 9 =$ ___ $14 \div 7 =$ ___ $6 \times 3 =$ ___ $6 \div 3 =$ ___ $18 \div 3 =$ ___

B. $12 \div 4 =$ ___ $3 \times 3 =$ ___ $56 \div 8 =$ ___ $12 \div 2 =$ ___ $0 \times 5 =$ ___

C. $5 \times 5 =$ ___ $18 \div 6 =$ ___ $4 \times 3 =$ ___ $8 \div 8 =$ ___ $25 \div 5 =$ ___

D. $14 \div 2 =$ ___ $4 \times 4 =$ ___ $4 \div 2 =$ ___ $16 \div 4 =$ ___ $7 \times 8 =$ ___

E. $1 \times 3 =$ ___ $0 \div 1 =$ ___ $16 \div 8 =$ ___ $12 \div 3 =$ ___ $7 \div 7 =$ ___

F. $56 \div 7 =$ ___ $3 \times 4 =$ ___ $18 \div 9 =$ ___ $6 \times 2 =$ ___ $12 \div 6 =$ ___

G. $25 \div 5 =$ ___ $10 \div 2 =$ ___ $9 \times 2 =$ ___ $16 \div 2 =$ ___ $18 \div 6 =$ ___

H. $9 \times 9 =$ ___ $12 \div 4 =$ ___ $2 \times 7 =$ ___ $8 \times 1 =$ ___ $3 \div 3 =$ ___

I. $81 \div 9 =$ ___ $8 \div 4 =$ ___ $9 \div 1 =$ ___ $9 \div 3 =$ ___ $3 \times 6 =$ ___

J. $12 \div 3 =$ ___ $18 \div 3 =$ ___ $8 \div 2 =$ ___ $1 \times 5 =$ ___ $16 \div 4 =$ ___

Name _____

Cumulative Division Practice. Review the division facts.

A. $1 \div 1 =$ ___ $18 \div 2 =$ ___ $56 \div 8 =$ ___ $0 \div 6 =$ ___ $14 \div 2 =$ ___

B. $12 \div 6 =$ ___ $12 \div 4 =$ ___ $8 \div 2 =$ ___ $16 \div 8 =$ ___ $9 \div 9 =$ ___

C. $4 \div 4 =$ ___ $6 \div 2 =$ ___ $2 \div 1 =$ ___ $4 \div 2 =$ ___ $18 \div 3 =$ ___

D. $18 \div 6 =$ ___ $3 \div 3 =$ ___ $5 \div 1 =$ ___ $6 \div 1 =$ ___ $12 \div 4 =$ ___

E. $16 \div 4 =$ ___ $56 \div 7 =$ ___ $0 \div 3 =$ ___ $8 \div 8 =$ ___ $81 \div 9 =$ ___

F. $14 \div 7 =$ ___ $12 \div 3 =$ ___ $10 \div 5 =$ ___ $6 \div 3 =$ ___ $3 \div 1 =$ ___

G. $7 \div 1 =$ ___ $5 \div 5 =$ ___ $9 \div 3 =$ ___ $0 \div 9 =$ ___ $2 \div 2 =$ ___

H. $0 \div 5 =$ ___ $18 \div 3 =$ ___ $4 \div 1 =$ ___ $7 \div 7 =$ ___ $18 \div 6 =$ ___

I. $18 \div 9 =$ ___ $12 \div 2 =$ ___ $16 \div 2 =$ ___ $8 \div 4 =$ ___ $10 \div 2 =$ ___

J. $6 \div 6 =$ ___ $9 \div 1 =$ ___ $25 \div 5 =$ ___ $12 \div 3 =$ ___ $8 \div 1 =$ ___

Ten Divided by Five Is Not Five: Using Multiplication to Make Division Easy

Name _____

Cumulative Division Practice. Review the division facts.

A. $1\overline{)2}$ $2\overline{)18}$ $2\overline{)4}$ $8\overline{)56}$ $5\overline{)25}$ $2\overline{)6}$

B. $4\overline{)12}$ $6\overline{)18}$ $3\overline{)3}$ $4\overline{)8}$ $1\overline{)1}$ $7\overline{)14}$

C. $3\overline{)9}$ $5\overline{)10}$ $4\overline{)16}$ $1\overline{)8}$ $3\overline{)18}$ $9\overline{)81}$

D. $7\overline{)7}$ $4\overline{)0}$ $7\overline{)56}$ $8\overline{)16}$ $5\overline{)5}$ $3\overline{)12}$

E. $12 \div 2 =$ ___ $9 \div 1 =$ ___ $81 \div 9 =$ ___ $7 \div 1 =$ ___ $6 \div 3 =$ ___

F. $2 \div 2 =$ ___ $6 \div 6 =$ ___ $3 \div 1 =$ ___ $0 \div 7 =$ ___ $12 \div 3 =$ ___

G. $4 \div 1 =$ ___ $56 \div 8 =$ ___ $10 \div 2 =$ ___ $16 \div 4 =$ ___ $9 \div 9 =$ ___

H. $25 \div 5 =$ ___ $16 \div 2 =$ ___ $8 \div 2 =$ ___ $12 \div 4 =$ ___ $8 \div 8 =$ ___

I. $18 \div 3 =$ ___ $6 \div 1 =$ ___ $4 \div 4 =$ ___ $56 \div 7 =$ ___ $5 \div 1 =$ ___

J. $4 \div 2 =$ ___ $14 \div 2 =$ ___ $12 \div 6 =$ ___ $18 \div 6 =$ ___ $18 \div 9 =$ ___

Ten Divided by Five Is Not Five: Using Multiplication to Make Division Easy

Name _____

Multiply.

A.
$\begin{array}{r}6\\ \times 6\\ \hline\end{array}$
$\begin{array}{r}8\\ \times 6\\ \hline\end{array}$
$\begin{array}{r}2\\ \times 7\\ \hline\end{array}$
$\begin{array}{r}4\\ \times 4\\ \hline\end{array}$
$\begin{array}{r}9\\ \times 4\\ \hline\end{array}$
$\begin{array}{r}9\\ \times 1\\ \hline\end{array}$
$\begin{array}{r}6\\ \times 3\\ \hline\end{array}$

B.
$\begin{array}{r}9\\ \times 7\\ \hline\end{array}$
$\begin{array}{r}2\\ \times 2\\ \hline\end{array}$
$\begin{array}{r}5\\ \times 3\\ \hline\end{array}$
$\begin{array}{r}2\\ \times 8\\ \hline\end{array}$
$\begin{array}{r}6\\ \times 8\\ \hline\end{array}$
$\begin{array}{r}3\\ \times 4\\ \hline\end{array}$
$\begin{array}{r}9\\ \times 9\\ \hline\end{array}$

C.
$\begin{array}{r}2\\ \times 3\\ \hline\end{array}$
$\begin{array}{r}4\\ \times 9\\ \hline\end{array}$
$\begin{array}{r}1\\ \times 7\\ \hline\end{array}$
$\begin{array}{r}7\\ \times 9\\ \hline\end{array}$
$\begin{array}{r}3\\ \times 6\\ \hline\end{array}$
$\begin{array}{r}7\\ \times 8\\ \hline\end{array}$
$\begin{array}{r}2\\ \times 5\\ \hline\end{array}$

D.
$\begin{array}{r}3\\ \times 5\\ \hline\end{array}$
$\begin{array}{r}5\\ \times 5\\ \hline\end{array}$
$\begin{array}{r}9\\ \times 2\\ \hline\end{array}$
$\begin{array}{r}4\\ \times 3\\ \hline\end{array}$
$\begin{array}{r}2\\ \times 4\\ \hline\end{array}$
$\begin{array}{r}4\\ \times 1\\ \hline\end{array}$
$\begin{array}{r}6\\ \times 2\\ \hline\end{array}$

E.
$\begin{array}{r}9\\ \times 9\\ \hline\end{array}$
$\begin{array}{r}5\\ \times 3\\ \hline\end{array}$
$\begin{array}{r}6\\ \times 3\\ \hline\end{array}$
$\begin{array}{r}1\\ \times 1\\ \hline\end{array}$
$\begin{array}{r}9\\ \times 7\\ \hline\end{array}$
$\begin{array}{r}3\\ \times 4\\ \hline\end{array}$
$\begin{array}{r}9\\ \times 0\\ \hline\end{array}$

F.
$\begin{array}{r}4\\ \times 9\\ \hline\end{array}$
$\begin{array}{r}8\\ \times 2\\ \hline\end{array}$
$\begin{array}{r}3\\ \times 3\\ \hline\end{array}$
$\begin{array}{r}3\\ \times 2\\ \hline\end{array}$
$\begin{array}{r}3\\ \times 5\\ \hline\end{array}$
$\begin{array}{r}8\\ \times 7\\ \hline\end{array}$
$\begin{array}{r}1\\ \times 9\\ \hline\end{array}$

G.
$\begin{array}{r}8\\ \times 6\\ \hline\end{array}$
$\begin{array}{r}5\\ \times 2\\ \hline\end{array}$
$\begin{array}{r}8\\ \times 1\\ \hline\end{array}$
$\begin{array}{r}0\\ \times 2\\ \hline\end{array}$
$\begin{array}{r}6\\ \times 6\\ \hline\end{array}$
$\begin{array}{r}2\\ \times 9\\ \hline\end{array}$
$\begin{array}{r}7\\ \times 9\\ \hline\end{array}$

H.
$\begin{array}{r}4\\ \times 2\\ \hline\end{array}$
$\begin{array}{r}2\\ \times 6\\ \hline\end{array}$
$\begin{array}{r}9\\ \times 4\\ \hline\end{array}$
$\begin{array}{r}6\\ \times 8\\ \hline\end{array}$
$\begin{array}{r}7\\ \times 2\\ \hline\end{array}$
$\begin{array}{r}3\\ \times 1\\ \hline\end{array}$
$\begin{array}{r}3\\ \times 6\\ \hline\end{array}$

Ten Divided by Five Is Not Five: Using Multiplication to Make Division Easy

Name _____

Find the missing factor.

A. $9 \times \underline{\quad} = 36$ $6 \times \underline{\quad} = 36$ $4 \times \underline{\quad} = 16$ $3 \times \underline{\quad} = 15$

B. $5 \times \underline{\quad} = 25$ $\underline{\quad} \times 1 = 2$ $\underline{\quad} \times 2 = 14$ $6 \times \underline{\quad} = 48$

C. $4 \times \underline{\quad} = 4$ $7 \times \underline{\quad} = 63$ $4 \times \underline{\quad} = 36$ $\underline{\quad} \times 3 = 18$

D. $2 \times \underline{\quad} = 10$ $5 \times \underline{\quad} = 15$ $\underline{\quad} \times 3 = 9$ $9 \times \underline{\quad} = 63$

E. $3 \times \underline{\quad} = 6$ $8 \times \underline{\quad} = 56$ $3 \times \underline{\quad} = 12$ $\underline{\quad} \times 8 = 48$

F. $\underline{\quad} \times 6 = 36$ $8 \times \underline{\quad} = 48$ $3 \times \underline{\quad} = 15$ $9 \times \underline{\quad} = 36$

G. $6 \times \underline{\quad} = 18$ $9 \times \underline{\quad} = 63$ $7 \times \underline{\quad} = 63$ $8 \times \underline{\quad} = 16$

H. $9 \times \underline{\quad} = 81$ $\underline{\quad} \times 4 = 36$ $2 \times \underline{\quad} = 12$ $5 \times \underline{\quad} = 15$

I. $\underline{\quad} \times 8 = 0$ $2 \times \underline{\quad} = 8$ $6 \times \underline{\quad} = 48$ $\underline{\quad} \times 4 = 12$

Ten Divided by Five Is Not Five: Using Multiplication to Make Division Easy

Name _____

Solve the problems.

A.   Ben's mom gave him $15 for lunch money. If Ben spent $5 each
     day, how many days could he buy lunch?

Answer: _____
_____

B.   On Friday, there was a sale on 2-pound packages of meat. Each
     package was $7. If Stacy's mother had $63 to spend, how many
     packages of meat could she purchase?

Answer: _____
_____

C.   On Wednesday, 61 third-grade students bought pizza for lunch
     and 9 brought a lunch from home. How many more third-grade
     students bought pizza for lunch? That same day, 54 second
     graders also bought pizza for lunch. Which grade bought more
     lunches on Wednesday?

Answer: _____
_____

D.   Farmer Jackson had 36 horses and 16 sheep. He wanted to fence
     his farm so that only 4 horses would be in each fenced space. How
     many spaces did he need for the horses?

Answer: _____
_____

E.   Erica has 4 different ribbon colors. She uses 48 inches of blue
     ribbon and cuts off pieces for her art project that are each 8 inches
     long. How many blue ribbon pieces will she have?

Answer: _____
_____

F.   Jenny's father gave her $36 to spend on clothes. She bought a
     T-shirt for $9, 4 pairs of socks for $4 each, and a sunhat for $8.
     How much money did she spend?

Answer: _____

Ten Divided by Five Is Not Five: Using Multiplication to Make Division Easy   **17**

Name _____

Divide.

A. $6 \div 2 =$ ___ $12 \div$ ___ $= 4$ $36 \div 6 =$ ___ $63 \div 9 =$ ___ $15 \div 3 =$ ___

B. $16 \div 4 =$ ___ $3 \div 3 =$ ___ $63 \div 7 =$ ___ $48 \div 6 =$ ___ $16 \div$ ___ $= 2$

C. $36 \div 9 =$ ___ $9 \div 3 =$ ___ $0 \div 3 =$ ___ $81 \div 9 =$ ___ $8 \div 4 =$ ___

D. $18 \div$ ___ $= 2$ $36 \div 4 =$ ___ $48 \div 8 =$ ___ $1 \div$ ___ $= 1$ $56 \div 8 =$ ___

E. $18 \div 6 =$ ___ $14 \div 7 =$ ___ $15 \div 5 =$ ___ $63 \div 7 =$ ___ $63 \div 9 =$ ___

F. $10 \div 5 =$ ___ $15 \div 3 =$ ___ $36 \div 9 =$ ___ $56 \div 7 =$ ___ $12 \div 4 =$ ___

G. $18 \div 3 =$ ___ $48 \div 6 =$ ___ $25 \div$ ___ $= 5$ $2 \div 1 =$ ___ $12 \div 6 =$ ___

H. $36 \div$ ___ $= 4$ $8 \div 1 =$ ___ $16 \div 4 =$ ___ $16 \div 8 =$ ___ $81 \div$ ___ $= 9$

I. $48 \div 8 =$ ___ $15 \div 3 =$ ___ $36 \div 6 =$ ___ $15 \div 5 =$ ___ $18 \div 3 =$ ___

J. $12 \div 3 =$ ___ $18 \div$ ___ $= 6$ $63 \div 7 =$ ___ $36 \div 4 =$ ___ $48 \div 6 =$ ___

Name _____

Divide.

A. $6\overline{)48}$ $3\overline{)12}$ $9\overline{)36}$ $3\overline{)15}$ $5\overline{)25}$ $6\overline{)36}$

B. $3\overline{)18}$ $2\overline{)8}$ $4\overline{)36}$ $6\overline{)12}$ $4\overline{)16}$ $7\overline{)63}$

C. $9\overline{)81}$ $8\overline{)48}$ $3\overline{)9}$ $6\overline{)18}$ $4\overline{)4}$ $5\overline{)15}$

D. $7\overline{)56}$ $9\overline{)63}$ $2\overline{)10}$ $4\overline{)36}$ $6\overline{)48}$ $6\overline{)18}$

E. $4\overline{)12}$ $9\overline{)18}$ $7\overline{)63}$ $2\overline{)12}$ $1\overline{)4}$ $2\overline{)14}$

F. $9\overline{)36}$ $3\overline{)6}$ $3\overline{)15}$ $9\overline{)63}$ $8\overline{)48}$ $6\overline{)0}$

G. $5\overline{)15}$ $8\overline{)16}$ $1\overline{)2}$ $6\overline{)6}$ $3\overline{)12}$ $9\overline{)63}$

H. $6\overline{)36}$ $2\overline{)4}$ $4\overline{)36}$ $8\overline{)48}$ $8\overline{)56}$ $3\overline{)15}$

Ten Divided by Five Is Not Five: Using Multiplication to Make Division Easy   **19**

Name _____

Divide and multiply.

A. $63 \div 9 =$ ___ $3 \div 1 =$ ___ $8 \times 6 =$ ___ $15 \div 5 =$ ___ $48 \div 6 =$ ___

B. $12 \div 4 =$ ___ $4 \times 9 =$ ___ $48 \div 8 =$ ___ $12 \div 6 =$ ___ $0 \times 7 =$ ___

C. $9 \times 7 =$ ___ $81 \div 9 =$ ___ $7 \times 2 =$ ___ $36 \div 4 =$ ___ $56 \div 7 =$ ___

D. $18 \div 6 =$ ___ $6 \times 6 =$ ___ $63 \div 7 =$ ___ $25 \div 5 =$ ___ $3 \times 5 =$ ___

E. $2 \times 9 =$ ___ $36 \div 9 =$ ___ $18 \div 3 =$ ___ $12 \div 3 =$ ___ $18 \div 2 =$ ___

F. $48 \div 6 =$ ___ $9 \times 4 =$ ___ $10 \div 2 =$ ___ $6 \times 1 =$ ___ $36 \div 4 =$ ___

G. $16 \div 2 =$ ___ $8 \div 4 =$ ___ $7 \times 9 =$ ___ $36 \div 6 =$ ___ $15 \div 3 =$ ___

H. $5 \times 3 =$ ___ $15 \div 5 =$ ___ $6 \times 8 =$ ___ $4 \times 3 =$ ___ $63 \div 7 =$ ___

I. $2 \div 2 =$ ___ $48 \div 8 =$ ___ $7 \div 7 =$ ___ $36 \div 9 =$ ___ $8 \times 7 =$ ___

J. $63 \div 9 =$ ___ $36 \div 6 =$ ___ $15 \div 3 =$ ___ $1 \times 7 =$ ___ $14 \div 2 =$ ___

Ten Divided by Five Is Not Five: Using Multiplication to Make Division Easy

Name _____

Cumulative Division Practice. Review the division facts.

A. $1\overline{)9}$ $4\overline{)36}$ $7\overline{)56}$ $8\overline{)48}$ $4\overline{)16}$ $5\overline{)15}$

B. $2\overline{)16}$ $9\overline{)63}$ $2\overline{)10}$ $6\overline{)18}$ $7\overline{)14}$ $4\overline{)12}$

C. $5\overline{)25}$ $9\overline{)81}$ $5\overline{)5}$ $6\overline{)36}$ $6\overline{)48}$ $2\overline{)6}$

D. $3\overline{)18}$ $7\overline{)63}$ $2\overline{)18}$ $1\overline{)0}$ $3\overline{)15}$ $1\overline{)6}$

E. $5\overline{)10}$ $3\overline{)12}$ $9\overline{)36}$ $4\overline{)8}$ $2\overline{)4}$ $4\overline{)36}$

F. $9\overline{)63}$ $2\overline{)14}$ $8\overline{)48}$ $9\overline{)18}$ $3\overline{)6}$ $7\overline{)63}$

G. $2\overline{)12}$ $6\overline{)48}$ $5\overline{)15}$ $1\overline{)5}$ $8\overline{)56}$ $2\overline{)8}$

H. $3\overline{)15}$ $1\overline{)7}$ $9\overline{)36}$ $2\overline{)0}$ $8\overline{)8}$ $6\overline{)36}$

Name _____

Cumulative Division Practice. Review the division facts.

A. $48 \div 6 =$ ___ $5 \div 1 =$ ___ $9 \div 3 =$ ___ $63 \div 9 =$ ___ $16 \div 4 =$ ___

B. $15 \div 5 =$ ___ $12 \div 3 =$ ___ $16 \div 2 =$ ___ $36 \div 4 =$ ___ $18 \div 6 =$ ___

C. $36 \div 9 =$ ___ $63 \div 7 =$ ___ $0 \div 4 =$ ___ $4 \div 4 =$ ___ $12 \div 6 =$ ___

D. $36 \div 6 =$ ___ $7 \div 7 =$ ___ $18 \div 2 =$ ___ $48 \div 8 =$ ___ $15 \div 5 =$ ___

E. $63 \div 9 =$ ___ $15 \div 3 =$ ___ $14 \div 7 =$ ___ $2 \div 1 =$ ___ $36 \div 4 =$ ___

F. $5 \div 5 =$ ___ $56 \div 8 =$ ___ $48 \div 6 =$ ___ $9 \div 9 =$ ___ $10 \div 2 =$ ___

G. $8 \div 2 =$ ___ $36 \div 9 =$ ___ $8 \div 1 =$ ___ $25 \div 5 =$ ___ $12 \div 4 =$ ___

H. $3 \div 1 =$ ___ $15 \div 5 =$ ___ $2 \div 2 =$ ___ $81 \div 9 =$ ___ $63 \div 9 =$ ___

I. $12 \div 3 =$ ___ $48 \div 8 =$ ___ $18 \div 9 =$ ___ $36 \div 9 =$ ___ $48 \div 6 =$ ___

J. $0 \div 3 =$ ___ $15 \div 3 =$ ___ $63 \div 7 =$ ___ $18 \div 3 =$ ___ $36 \div 6 =$ ___

Name _____

Multiply.

A.
$\begin{array}{r} 5 \\ \times\,4 \\ \hline \end{array}$
$\begin{array}{r} 8 \\ \times\,3 \\ \hline \end{array}$
$\begin{array}{r} 5 \\ \times\,5 \\ \hline \end{array}$
$\begin{array}{r} 5 \\ \times\,9 \\ \hline \end{array}$
$\begin{array}{r} 3 \\ \times\,8 \\ \hline \end{array}$
$\begin{array}{r} 4 \\ \times\,0 \\ \hline \end{array}$
$\begin{array}{r} 3 \\ \times\,5 \\ \hline \end{array}$

B.
$\begin{array}{r} 7 \\ \times\,8 \\ \hline \end{array}$
$\begin{array}{r} 9 \\ \times\,6 \\ \hline \end{array}$
$\begin{array}{r} 1 \\ \times\,5 \\ \hline \end{array}$
$\begin{array}{r} 3 \\ \times\,4 \\ \hline \end{array}$
$\begin{array}{r} 5 \\ \times\,3 \\ \hline \end{array}$
$\begin{array}{r} 3 \\ \times\,3 \\ \hline \end{array}$
$\begin{array}{r} 8 \\ \times\,6 \\ \hline \end{array}$

C.
$\begin{array}{r} 5 \\ \times\,9 \\ \hline \end{array}$
$\begin{array}{r} 9 \\ \times\,4 \\ \hline \end{array}$
$\begin{array}{r} 6 \\ \times\,9 \\ \hline \end{array}$
$\begin{array}{r} 4 \\ \times\,5 \\ \hline \end{array}$
$\begin{array}{r} 2 \\ \times\,2 \\ \hline \end{array}$
$\begin{array}{r} 9 \\ \times\,9 \\ \hline \end{array}$
$\begin{array}{r} 4 \\ \times\,3 \\ \hline \end{array}$

D.
$\begin{array}{r} 6 \\ \times\,6 \\ \hline \end{array}$
$\begin{array}{r} 2 \\ \times\,6 \\ \hline \end{array}$
$\begin{array}{r} 8 \\ \times\,3 \\ \hline \end{array}$
$\begin{array}{r} 9 \\ \times\,7 \\ \hline \end{array}$
$\begin{array}{r} 4 \\ \times\,2 \\ \hline \end{array}$
$\begin{array}{r} 9 \\ \times\,5 \\ \hline \end{array}$
$\begin{array}{r} 6 \\ \times\,1 \\ \hline \end{array}$

E.
$\begin{array}{r} 9 \\ \times\,6 \\ \hline \end{array}$
$\begin{array}{r} 5 \\ \times\,9 \\ \hline \end{array}$
$\begin{array}{r} 2 \\ \times\,3 \\ \hline \end{array}$
$\begin{array}{r} 3 \\ \times\,8 \\ \hline \end{array}$
$\begin{array}{r} 6 \\ \times\,3 \\ \hline \end{array}$
$\begin{array}{r} 2 \\ \times\,9 \\ \hline \end{array}$
$\begin{array}{r} 5 \\ \times\,4 \\ \hline \end{array}$

F.
$\begin{array}{r} 4 \\ \times\,5 \\ \hline \end{array}$
$\begin{array}{r} 0 \\ \times\,6 \\ \hline \end{array}$
$\begin{array}{r} 4 \\ \times\,9 \\ \hline \end{array}$
$\begin{array}{r} 4 \\ \times\,4 \\ \hline \end{array}$
$\begin{array}{r} 8 \\ \times\,6 \\ \hline \end{array}$
$\begin{array}{r} 5 \\ \times\,4 \\ \hline \end{array}$
$\begin{array}{r} 7 \\ \times\,9 \\ \hline \end{array}$

G.
$\begin{array}{r} 3 \\ \times\,6 \\ \hline \end{array}$
$\begin{array}{r} 2 \\ \times\,8 \\ \hline \end{array}$
$\begin{array}{r} 6 \\ \times\,9 \\ \hline \end{array}$
$\begin{array}{r} 9 \\ \times\,7 \\ \hline \end{array}$
$\begin{array}{r} 9 \\ \times\,4 \\ \hline \end{array}$
$\begin{array}{r} 7 \\ \times\,2 \\ \hline \end{array}$
$\begin{array}{r} 3 \\ \times\,5 \\ \hline \end{array}$

H.
$\begin{array}{r} 6 \\ \times\,8 \\ \hline \end{array}$
$\begin{array}{r} 8 \\ \times\,3 \\ \hline \end{array}$
$\begin{array}{r} 5 \\ \times\,2 \\ \hline \end{array}$
$\begin{array}{r} 6 \\ \times\,6 \\ \hline \end{array}$
$\begin{array}{r} 1 \\ \times\,3 \\ \hline \end{array}$
$\begin{array}{r} 9 \\ \times\,5 \\ \hline \end{array}$
$\begin{array}{r} 9 \\ \times\,6 \\ \hline \end{array}$

Ten Divided by Five Is Not Five: Using Multiplication to Make Division Easy

Name _____

Find the missing factor.

A. $7 \times \underline{\hphantom{00}} = 7$ $3 \times \underline{\hphantom{00}} = 18$ $2 \times \underline{\hphantom{00}} = 6$ $4 \times \underline{\hphantom{00}} = 12$

B. $9 \times \underline{\hphantom{00}} = 45$ $\underline{\hphantom{00}} \times 5 = 20$ $\underline{\hphantom{00}} \times 9 = 54$ $5 \times \underline{\hphantom{00}} = 45$

C. $4 \times \underline{\hphantom{00}} = 20$ $7 \times \underline{\hphantom{00}} = 63$ $4 \times \underline{\hphantom{00}} = 36$ $\underline{\hphantom{00}} \times 5 = 15$

D. $9 \times \underline{\hphantom{00}} = 36$ $6 \times \underline{\hphantom{00}} = 36$ $\underline{\hphantom{00}} \times 8 = 16$ $7 \times \underline{\hphantom{00}} = 56$

E. $8 \times \underline{\hphantom{00}} = 24$ $6 \times \underline{\hphantom{00}} = 48$ $3 \times \underline{\hphantom{00}} = 12$ $\underline{\hphantom{00}} \times 3 = 24$

F. $\underline{\hphantom{00}} \times 5 = 5$ $1 \times \underline{\hphantom{00}} = 1$ $6 \times \underline{\hphantom{00}} = 54$ $5 \times \underline{\hphantom{00}} = 25$

G. $6 \times \underline{\hphantom{00}} = 18$ $9 \times \underline{\hphantom{00}} = 0$ $3 \times \underline{\hphantom{00}} = 15$ $3 \times \underline{\hphantom{00}} = 24$

H. $2 \times \underline{\hphantom{00}} = 18$ $\underline{\hphantom{00}} \times 6 = 48$ $4 \times \underline{\hphantom{00}} = 16$ $5 \times \underline{\hphantom{00}} = 20$

I. $\underline{\hphantom{00}} \times 9 = 63$ $5 \times \underline{\hphantom{00}} = 25$ $9 \times \underline{\hphantom{00}} = 54$ $\underline{\hphantom{00}} \times 5 = 45$

  Ten Divided by Five Is Not Five: Using Multiplication to Make Division Easy

Name _____

Solve the problems.

A. In Jenn's school, 36 teachers are men and 45 are women.
On Monday, 9 teachers were absent. How many teachers
were at school?

Answer: _____

B. Jacob's mom baked 45 chocolate muffins. She had 8 ziplock
bags and put 5 muffins in each bag. How many more bags did
she need?

Answer: _____

C. Dad bought 4 boxes of wheat crackers and 1 bag of pretzels.
There are 18 crackers in each box and 24 pretzels in each bag.
There were 3 children, and mom said they could share the pretzels
evenly. How many pretzels did each child get?

Answer: _____

D. On Tuesday, the music class rode in vans to go to a concert.
There were 63 students. If each van fit 9 students, and it cost $7
to rent each van, how much money did they need for the vans?

Answer: _____

E. Mr. Zev's pet and fish store has 20 different kinds of fish. He has
2 counters to hold fish tanks and likes to keep 4 different kinds of
fish in each tank. How many tanks does he need?

Answer: _____

F. Jon's gym class had 62 students. At 11 a.m., 8 students left the
room for extra math help. How many students remained? If 9 were
on each team, how many teams were there?

Answer: _____

Ten Divided by Five Is Not Five: Using Multiplication to Make Division Easy

Name _____

Divide.

A. $36 \div 6 = \_\_\_$ $15 \div \_\_\_ = 3$ $20 \div 5 = \_\_\_$ $45 \div 5 = \_\_\_$ $54 \div 9 = \_\_\_$

B. $12 \div 2 = \_\_\_$ $24 \div 3 = \_\_\_$ $45 \div 9 = \_\_\_$ $1 \div 1 = \_\_\_$ $36 \div \_\_\_ = 9$

C. $63 \div 7 = \_\_\_$ $25 \div 5 = \_\_\_$ $12 \div 3 = \_\_\_$ $4 \div 2 = \_\_\_$ $4 \div 1 = \_\_\_$

D. $18 \div \_\_\_ = 3$ $54 \div 6 = \_\_\_$ $16 \div 8 = \_\_\_$ $9 \div \_\_\_ = 1$ $24 \div 3 = \_\_\_$

E. $20 \div 5 = \_\_\_$ $56 \div 7 = \_\_\_$ $20 \div 4 = \_\_\_$ $15 \div 5 = \_\_\_$ $18 \div 2 = \_\_\_$

F. $54 \div 9 = \_\_\_$ $36 \div 9 = \_\_\_$ $81 \div 9 = \_\_\_$ $48 \div 8 = \_\_\_$ $63 \div 9 = \_\_\_$

G. $8 \div 8 = \_\_\_$ $45 \div 9 = \_\_\_$ $24 \div \_\_\_ = 8$ $16 \div 4 = \_\_\_$ $8 \div 4 = \_\_\_$

H. $45 \div \_\_\_ = 9$ $24 \div 3 = \_\_\_$ $6 \div 3 = \_\_\_$ $20 \div 4 = \_\_\_$ $48 \div \_\_\_ = 8$

I. $54 \div 6 = \_\_\_$ $14 \div 7 = \_\_\_$ $12 \div 4 = \_\_\_$ $0 \div 5 = \_\_\_$ $24 \div 8 = \_\_\_$

J. $45 \div 5 = \_\_\_$ $20 \div \_\_\_ = 5$ $10 \div 2 = \_\_\_$ $54 \div 9 = \_\_\_$ $6 \div 6 = \_\_\_$

Name _____

Divide.

A. $4\overline{)36}$ $3\overline{)15}$ $9\overline{)81}$ $9\overline{)54}$ $2\overline{)4}$ $5\overline{)20}$

B. $3\overline{)12}$ $1\overline{)2}$ $3\overline{)18}$ $3\overline{)24}$ $8\overline{)48}$ $7\overline{)63}$

C. $9\overline{)45}$ $9\overline{)63}$ $4\overline{)20}$ $8\overline{)24}$ $6\overline{)12}$ $6\overline{)36}$

D. $5\overline{)20}$ $5\overline{)45}$ $5\overline{)15}$ $8\overline{)56}$ $1\overline{)0}$ $6\overline{)54}$

E. $9\overline{)54}$ $8\overline{)24}$ $5\overline{)10}$ $3\overline{)3}$ $9\overline{)45}$ $4\overline{)20}$

F. $6\overline{)48}$ $2\overline{)14}$ $9\overline{)36}$ $5\overline{)25}$ $5\overline{)45}$ $7\overline{)56}$

G. $4\overline{)16}$ $9\overline{)45}$ $3\overline{)24}$ $4\overline{)20}$ $6\overline{)54}$ $8\overline{)48}$

H. $7\overline{)63}$ $4\overline{)36}$ $4\overline{)8}$ $9\overline{)54}$ $3\overline{)15}$ $8\overline{)24}$

Ten Divided by Five Is Not Five: Using Multiplication to Make Division Easy **27**

Name _____

Divide and multiply.

A. $45 \div 9 =$ ___ $0 \div 7 =$ ___ $8 \times 3 =$ ___ $24 \div 8 =$ ___ $56 \div 7 =$ ___

B. $63 \div 7 =$ ___ $6 \times 9 =$ ___ $36 \div 6 =$ ___ $18 \div 3 =$ ___ $5 \times 9 =$ ___

C. $9 \times 4 =$ ___ $54 \div 9 =$ ___ $6 \times 8 =$ ___ $45 \div 5 =$ ___ $36 \div 9 =$ ___

D. $6 \div 2 =$ ___ $7 \times 8 =$ ___ $20 \div 4 =$ ___ $12 \div 3 =$ ___ $9 \times 6 =$ ___

E. $9 \times 7 =$ ___ $15 \div 3 =$ ___ $45 \div 5 =$ ___ $48 \div 8 =$ ___ $6 \div 2 =$ ___

F. $24 \div 3 =$ ___ $5 \times 4 =$ ___ $6 \div 1 =$ ___ $3 \times 6 =$ ___ $63 \div 9 =$ ___

G. $54 \div 9 =$ ___ $14 \div 7 =$ ___ $5 \times 2 =$ ___ $5 \div 5 =$ ___ $20 \div 5 =$ ___

H. $3 \times 2 =$ ___ $36 \div 4 =$ ___ $3 \times 5 =$ ___ $3 \times 8 =$ ___ $54 \div 6 =$ ___

I. $48 \div 6 =$ ___ $24 \div 8 =$ ___ $20 \div 5 =$ ___ $54 \div 6 =$ ___ $9 \times 1 =$ ___

J. $15 \div 5 =$ ___ $9 \div 3 =$ ___ $81 \div 9 =$ ___ $4 \times 5 =$ ___ $20 \div 4 =$ ___

Ten Divided by Five Is Not Five: Using Multiplication to Make Division Easy

Name _____

Cumulative Division Practice. Review the division facts.

A. $2\overline{)6}$ $5\overline{)25}$ $9\overline{)63}$ $9\overline{)54}$ $4\overline{)12}$ $9\overline{)36}$

B. $8\overline{)24}$ $9\overline{)18}$ $8\overline{)56}$ $3\overline{)15}$ $5\overline{)45}$ $5\overline{)20}$

C. $6\overline{)54}$ $8\overline{)48}$ $1\overline{)3}$ $2\overline{)12}$ $4\overline{)16}$ $9\overline{)45}$

D. $4\overline{)20}$ $8\overline{)24}$ $9\overline{)0}$ $4\overline{)36}$ $5\overline{)20}$ $3\overline{)24}$

E. $9\overline{)45}$ $6\overline{)6}$ $6\overline{)18}$ $6\overline{)36}$ $9\overline{)54}$ $6\overline{)48}$

F. $8\overline{)16}$ $5\overline{)15}$ $5\overline{)20}$ $8\overline{)0}$ $2\overline{)8}$ $4\overline{)4}$

G. $5\overline{)45}$ $7\overline{)14}$ $1\overline{)1}$ $3\overline{)9}$ $8\overline{)24}$ $6\overline{)54}$

H. $3\overline{)24}$ $7\overline{)63}$ $4\overline{)20}$ $6\overline{)54}$ $2\overline{)10}$ $9\overline{)45}$

    Ten Divided by Five Is Not Five: Using Multiplication to Make Division Easy

Name _____

Cumulative Division Practice. Review the division facts.

A. $81 \div 9 =$ ___ $15 \div 5 =$ ___ $54 \div 6 =$ ___ $20 \div 4 =$ ___ $63 \div 7 =$ ___

B. $24 \div 3 =$ ___ $45 \div 5 =$ ___ $9 \div 1 =$ ___ $8 \div 2 =$ ___ $36 \div 9 =$ ___

C. $45 \div 9 =$ ___ $7 \div 7 =$ ___ $48 \div 6 =$ ___ $24 \div 8 =$ ___ $20 \div 5 =$ ___

D. $16 \div 8 =$ ___ $54 \div 9 =$ ___ $12 \div 3 =$ ___ $56 \div 7 =$ ___ $6 \div 3 =$ ___

E. $20 \div 5 =$ ___ $63 \div 9 =$ ___ $36 \div 4 =$ ___ $16 \div 2 =$ ___ $12 \div 6 =$ ___

F. $54 \div 6 =$ ___ $36 \div 6 =$ ___ $48 \div 8 =$ ___ $45 \div 5 =$ ___ $4 \div 1 =$ ___

G. $2 \div 2 =$ ___ $10 \div 5 =$ ___ $8 \div 4 =$ ___ $25 \div 5 =$ ___ $24 \div 8 =$ ___

H. $20 \div 4 =$ ___ $18 \div 3 =$ ___ $45 \div 9 =$ ___ $4 \div 2 =$ ___ $18 \div 2 =$ ___

I. $10 \div 2 =$ ___ $0 \div 8 =$ ___ $56 \div 8 =$ ___ $15 \div 3 =$ ___ $12 \div 4 =$ ___

J. $24 \div 3 =$ ___ $54 \div 9 =$ ___ $7 \div 1 =$ ___ $6 \div 2 =$ ___ $16 \div 4 =$ ___

Ten Divided by Five Is Not Five: Using Multiplication to Make Division Easy

Name _____

Multiply.

A.
$\begin{array}{r} 8 \\ \times\, 5 \\ \hline \end{array}$
$\begin{array}{r} 5 \\ \times\, 5 \\ \hline \end{array}$
$\begin{array}{r} 8 \\ \times\, 6 \\ \hline \end{array}$
$\begin{array}{r} 6 \\ \times\, 2 \\ \hline \end{array}$
$\begin{array}{r} 7 \\ \times\, 4 \\ \hline \end{array}$
$\begin{array}{r} 5 \\ \times\, 6 \\ \hline \end{array}$
$\begin{array}{r} 2 \\ \times\, 1 \\ \hline \end{array}$

B.
$\begin{array}{r} 4 \\ \times\, 6 \\ \hline \end{array}$
$\begin{array}{r} 4 \\ \times\, 9 \\ \hline \end{array}$
$\begin{array}{r} 7 \\ \times\, 9 \\ \hline \end{array}$
$\begin{array}{r} 8 \\ \times\, 3 \\ \hline \end{array}$
$\begin{array}{r} 9 \\ \times\, 5 \\ \hline \end{array}$
$\begin{array}{r} 7 \\ \times\, 7 \\ \hline \end{array}$
$\begin{array}{r} 5 \\ \times\, 8 \\ \hline \end{array}$

C.
$\begin{array}{r} 6 \\ \times\, 6 \\ \hline \end{array}$
$\begin{array}{r} 1 \\ \times\, 8 \\ \hline \end{array}$
$\begin{array}{r} 6 \\ \times\, 4 \\ \hline \end{array}$
$\begin{array}{r} 4 \\ \times\, 3 \\ \hline \end{array}$
$\begin{array}{r} 8 \\ \times\, 8 \\ \hline \end{array}$
$\begin{array}{r} 2 \\ \times\, 4 \\ \hline \end{array}$
$\begin{array}{r} 6 \\ \times\, 5 \\ \hline \end{array}$

D.
$\begin{array}{r} 5 \\ \times\, 4 \\ \hline \end{array}$
$\begin{array}{r} 5 \\ \times\, 9 \\ \hline \end{array}$
$\begin{array}{r} 5 \\ \times\, 3 \\ \hline \end{array}$
$\begin{array}{r} 4 \\ \times\, 7 \\ \hline \end{array}$
$\begin{array}{r} 6 \\ \times\, 9 \\ \hline \end{array}$
$\begin{array}{r} 6 \\ \times\, 3 \\ \hline \end{array}$
$\begin{array}{r} 4 \\ \times\, 6 \\ \hline \end{array}$

E.
$\begin{array}{r} 8 \\ \times\, 7 \\ \hline \end{array}$
$\begin{array}{r} 2 \\ \times\, 7 \\ \hline \end{array}$
$\begin{array}{r} 6 \\ \times\, 8 \\ \hline \end{array}$
$\begin{array}{r} 4 \\ \times\, 5 \\ \hline \end{array}$
$\begin{array}{r} 3 \\ \times\, 2 \\ \hline \end{array}$
$\begin{array}{r} 6 \\ \times\, 4 \\ \hline \end{array}$
$\begin{array}{r} 8 \\ \times\, 5 \\ \hline \end{array}$

F.
$\begin{array}{r} 5 \\ \times\, 6 \\ \hline \end{array}$
$\begin{array}{r} 3 \\ \times\, 4 \\ \hline \end{array}$
$\begin{array}{r} 7 \\ \times\, 0 \\ \hline \end{array}$
$\begin{array}{r} 9 \\ \times\, 5 \\ \hline \end{array}$
$\begin{array}{r} 8 \\ \times\, 5 \\ \hline \end{array}$
$\begin{array}{r} 3 \\ \times\, 8 \\ \hline \end{array}$
$\begin{array}{r} 4 \\ \times\, 7 \\ \hline \end{array}$

G.
$\begin{array}{r} 7 \\ \times\, 7 \\ \hline \end{array}$
$\begin{array}{r} 3 \\ \times\, 5 \\ \hline \end{array}$
$\begin{array}{r} 9 \\ \times\, 6 \\ \hline \end{array}$
$\begin{array}{r} 5 \\ \times\, 6 \\ \hline \end{array}$
$\begin{array}{r} 1 \\ \times\, 4 \\ \hline \end{array}$
$\begin{array}{r} 5 \\ \times\, 8 \\ \hline \end{array}$
$\begin{array}{r} 6 \\ \times\, 5 \\ \hline \end{array}$

H.
$\begin{array}{r} 7 \\ \times\, 4 \\ \hline \end{array}$
$\begin{array}{r} 8 \\ \times\, 3 \\ \hline \end{array}$
$\begin{array}{r} 4 \\ \times\, 5 \\ \hline \end{array}$
$\begin{array}{r} 4 \\ \times\, 6 \\ \hline \end{array}$
$\begin{array}{r} 8 \\ \times\, 8 \\ \hline \end{array}$
$\begin{array}{r} 4 \\ \times\, 7 \\ \hline \end{array}$
$\begin{array}{r} 6 \\ \times\, 9 \\ \hline \end{array}$

SECTION 5

Ten Divided by Five Is Not Five: Using Multiplication to Make Division Easy

Name _____

Find the missing factor.

A. $1 \times \underline{\hspace{1cm}} = 8$ $8 \times \underline{\hspace{1cm}} = 40$ $7 \times \underline{\hspace{1cm}} = 49$ $4 \times \underline{\hspace{1cm}} = 24$

B. $3 \times \underline{\hspace{1cm}} = 24$ $\underline{\hspace{1cm}} \times 2 = 4$ $\underline{\hspace{1cm}} \times 6 = 54$ $4 \times \underline{\hspace{1cm}} = 28$

C. $5 \times \underline{\hspace{1cm}} = 40$ $4 \times \underline{\hspace{1cm}} = 36$ $5 \times \underline{\hspace{1cm}} = 20$ $\underline{\hspace{1cm}} \times 7 = 56$

D. $8 \times \underline{\hspace{1cm}} = 48$ $1 \times \underline{\hspace{1cm}} = 3$ $\underline{\hspace{1cm}} \times 7 = 63$ $5 \times \underline{\hspace{1cm}} = 30$

E. $9 \times \underline{\hspace{1cm}} = 81$ $7 \times \underline{\hspace{1cm}} = 28$ $2 \times \underline{\hspace{1cm}} = 14$ $\underline{\hspace{1cm}} \times 3 = 15$

F. $\underline{\hspace{1cm}} \times 7 = 49$ $2 \times \underline{\hspace{1cm}} = 10$ $6 \times \underline{\hspace{1cm}} = 30$ $5 \times \underline{\hspace{1cm}} = 45$

G. $4 \times \underline{\hspace{1cm}} = 28$ $4 \times \underline{\hspace{1cm}} = 24$ $5 \times \underline{\hspace{1cm}} = 30$ $8 \times \underline{\hspace{1cm}} = 64$

H. $9 \times \underline{\hspace{1cm}} = 54$ $\underline{\hspace{1cm}} \times 4 = 20$ $1 \times \underline{\hspace{1cm}} = 0$ $6 \times \underline{\hspace{1cm}} = 24$

I. $\underline{\hspace{1cm}} \times 8 = 24$ $9 \times \underline{\hspace{1cm}} = 45$ $7 \times \underline{\hspace{1cm}} = 28$ $\underline{\hspace{1cm}} \times 5 = 40$

Ten Divided by Five Is Not Five: Using Multiplication to Make Division Easy

Name _____

Solve the problems.

A. Alex was told he would need 30 pounds of dog food for his dog
    to eat each week. If his dog eats 5 pounds a day, will he have
    enough for the week?

Answer: _____

_____

B. Mom spent a total of $64 on 8 large boxes of Healthy Grain cereal.
    How much did each box of cereal cost?

Answer: _____

_____

C. Miss Wald wants a soft rug for her classroom. She wants to
    cover a section of her room that is 6 feet wide by 9 feet long.
    The principal ordered a square rug that is 8 feet on one side.
    How much larger is that rug than what she wants?

Answer: _____

_____

D. Abby planned a vegetable garden with 4 different vegetables.
    The green bean seed packet had 40 seeds. If she plants 8 rows
    of green beans, how many seeds will be in each row?

Answer: _____

_____

E. There were 12 vanilla cookies and 12 chocolate cookies in the
    cookie jar. Grandma gave Eli the cookie jar and asked him to put
    4 cookies on each plate. How many plates did Eli need?

Answer: _____

_____

F. Louis has $28. How many packs of baseball cards can he buy for
    $4 each? If each pack has 9 cards, and he wants to give away
    48 cards to friends at his party, how many cards will he have left?

Answer: _____

Ten Divided by Five Is Not Five: Using Multiplication to Make Division Easy

Name _____

Divide.

A. $24 \div 6 =$ ____ $49 \div$ ____ $= 7$ $54 \div 6 =$ ____ $24 \div 3 =$ ____ $36 \div 4 =$ ____

B. $30 \div 5 =$ ____ $40 \div 8 =$ ____ $15 \div 3 =$ ____ $48 \div 8 =$ ____ $20 \div$ ____ $= 4$

C. $45 \div 9 =$ ____ $30 \div 6 =$ ____ $64 \div 8 =$ ____ $24 \div 4 =$ ____ $28 \div 7 =$ ____

D. $63 \div$ ____ $= 7$ $40 \div 5 =$ ____ $56 \div 7 =$ ____ $40 \div$ ____ $= 5$ $10 \div 5 =$ ____

E. $28 \div 7 =$ ____ $20 \div 4 =$ ____ $24 \div 6 =$ ____ $28 \div 4 =$ ____ $45 \div 9 =$ ____

F. $24 \div 8 =$ ____ $64 \div 8 =$ ____ $30 \div 6 =$ ____ $40 \div 5 =$ ____ $2 \div 1 =$ ____

G. $45 \div 5 =$ ____ $12 \div 2 =$ ____ $36 \div$ ____ $= 6$ $14 \div 2 =$ ____ $30 \div 5 =$ ____

H. $24 \div$ ____ $= 3$ $0 \div 6 =$ ____ $9 \div 3 =$ ____ $28 \div 7 =$ ____ $24 \div$ ____ $= 4$

I. $30 \div 5 =$ ____ $18 \div 9 =$ ____ $49 \div 7 =$ ____ $54 \div 6 =$ ____ $28 \div 4 =$ ____

J. $40 \div 8 =$ ____ $54 \div$ ____ $= 6$ $24 \div 4 =$ ____ $20 \div 5 =$ ____ $4 \div 2 =$ ____

34   Ten Divided by Five Is Not Five: Using Multiplication to Make Division Easy

Name _____

Divide.

A. $4\overline{)24}$ $8\overline{)40}$ $6\overline{)30}$ $5\overline{)40}$ $8\overline{)64}$ $9\overline{)36}$

B. $9\overline{)45}$ $4\overline{)20}$ $4\overline{)28}$ $5\overline{)25}$ $9\overline{)54}$ $5\overline{)30}$

C. $3\overline{)24}$ $7\overline{)28}$ $5\overline{)45}$ $6\overline{)24}$ $1\overline{)8}$ $7\overline{)49}$

D. $8\overline{)56}$ $2\overline{)12}$ $4\overline{)24}$ $6\overline{)30}$ $5\overline{)40}$ $4\overline{)20}$

E. $3\overline{)6}$ $8\overline{)24}$ $4\overline{)0}$ $4\overline{)8}$ $4\overline{)28}$ $5\overline{)5}$

F. $7\overline{)49}$ $5\overline{)45}$ $5\overline{)30}$ $7\overline{)28}$ $4\overline{)12}$ $6\overline{)48}$

G. $2\overline{)16}$ $3\overline{)24}$ $8\overline{)40}$ $8\overline{)64}$ $6\overline{)24}$ $5\overline{)40}$

H. $9\overline{)54}$ $4\overline{)28}$ $4\overline{)24}$ $5\overline{)20}$ $6\overline{)30}$ $6\overline{)54}$

SECTION 5

    Ten Divided by Five Is Not Five: Using Multiplication to Make Division Easy   **35**

Name _____

Divide and multiply.

A. $64 \div 8 =$ ___ $40 \div 8 =$ ___ $8 \times 5 =$ ___ $24 \div 8 =$ ___ $30 \div 6 =$ ___

B. $24 \div 6 =$ ___ $6 \times 4 =$ ___ $30 \div 5 =$ ___ $48 \div 6 =$ ___ $4 \times 7 =$ ___

C. $3 \times 4 =$ ___ $28 \div 4 =$ ___ $7 \times 7 =$ ___ $54 \div 6 =$ ___ $24 \div 4 =$ ___

D. $81 \div 9 =$ ___ $8 \times 8 =$ ___ $40 \div 5 =$ ___ $12 \div 3 =$ ___ $8 \times 2 =$ ___

E. $5 \times 6 =$ ___ $45 \div 5 =$ ___ $28 \div 7 =$ ___ $5 \div 1 =$ ___ $24 \div 4 =$ ___

F. $16 \div 8 =$ ___ $7 \times 4 =$ ___ $4 \div 4 =$ ___ $6 \times 1 =$ ___ $40 \div 8 =$ ___

G. $28 \div 4 =$ ___ $49 \div 7 =$ ___ $4 \times 5 =$ ___ $30 \div 6 =$ ___ $18 \div 6 =$ ___

H. $8 \times 3 =$ ___ $30 \div 5 =$ ___ $5 \times 8 =$ ___ $4 \times 6 =$ ___ $24 \div 6 =$ ___

I. $40 \div 5 =$ ___ $45 \div 9 =$ ___ $20 \div 4 =$ ___ $28 \div 7 =$ ___ $6 \times 5 =$ ___

J. $54 \div 9 =$ ___ $20 \div 5 =$ ___ $64 \div 8 =$ ___ $9 \times 5 =$ ___ $24 \div 3 =$ ___

Name _____

Divide.

A. $8\overline{)64}$ $6\overline{)30}$ $9\overline{)18}$ $8\overline{)48}$ $8\overline{)24}$ $4\overline{)28}$

B. $5\overline{)40}$ $1\overline{)6}$ $4\overline{)24}$ $9\overline{)45}$ $5\overline{)25}$ $3\overline{)15}$

C. $7\overline{)28}$ $6\overline{)24}$ $7\overline{)63}$ $7\overline{)49}$ $4\overline{)16}$ $8\overline{)40}$

D. $4\overline{)20}$ $4\overline{)28}$ $2\overline{)6}$ $9\overline{)81}$ $7\overline{)56}$ $5\overline{)40}$

E. $5\overline{)45}$ $3\overline{)0}$ $6\overline{)30}$ $3\overline{)18}$ $5\overline{)30}$ $8\overline{)64}$

F. $3\overline{)24}$ $6\overline{)54}$ $7\overline{)49}$ $4\overline{)24}$ $8\overline{)40}$ $1\overline{)4}$

G. $9\overline{)54}$ $5\overline{)15}$ $5\overline{)20}$ $5\overline{)30}$ $3\overline{)9}$ $6\overline{)24}$

H. $8\overline{)8}$ $5\overline{)10}$ $4\overline{)24}$ $7\overline{)28}$ $6\overline{)36}$ $7\overline{)49}$

Ten Divided by Five Is Not Five: Using Multiplication to Make Division Easy

Name _____

Divide.

A. $30 \div 5 =$ ___ $48 \div$ ___ $= 6$ $24 \div 8 =$ ___ $36 \div 6 =$ ___ $0 \div 2 =$ ___

B. $16 \div 8 =$ ___ $28 \div 7 =$ ___ $54 \div 9 =$ ___ $20 \div 4 =$ ___ $45 \div$ ___ $= 5$

C. $10 \div 2 =$ ___ $30 \div 6 =$ ___ $24 \div 6 =$ ___ $40 \div 5 =$ ___ $63 \div 7 =$ ___

D. $12 \div$ ___ $= 2$ $40 \div 8 =$ ___ $1 \div 1 =$ ___ $18 \div$ ___ $= 9$ $49 \div 7 =$ ___

E. $24 \div 4 =$ ___ $64 \div 8 =$ ___ $30 \div 6 =$ ___ $45 \div 9 =$ ___ $56 \div 8 =$ ___

F. $36 \div 4 =$ ___ $24 \div 8 =$ ___ $40 \div 5 =$ ___ $54 \div 9 =$ ___ $28 \div 4 =$ ___

G. $20 \div 5 =$ ___ $45 \div 5 =$ ___ $8 \div$ ___ $= 4$ $16 \div 2 =$ ___ $24 \div 3 =$ ___

H. $28 \div$ ___ $= 4$ $24 \div 6 =$ ___ $28 \div 4 =$ ___ $15 \div 5 =$ ___ $64 \div$ ___ $= 8$

I. $14 \div 7 =$ ___ $36 \div 9 =$ ___ $30 \div 5 =$ ___ $63 \div 9 =$ ___ $10 \div 2 =$ ___

J. $49 \div 7 =$ ___ $3 \div$ ___ $= 3$ $54 \div 6 =$ ___ $40 \div 8 =$ ___ $24 \div 4 =$ ___

Ten Divided by Five Is Not Five: Using Multiplication to Make Division Easy

Name _____

Cumulative Division Practice. Review the division facts.

A. $6\overline{)30}$ $9\overline{)45}$ $4\overline{)36}$ $3\overline{)12}$ $2\overline{)4}$ $7\overline{)49}$

B. $4\overline{)24}$ $7\overline{)28}$ $2\overline{)14}$ $5\overline{)40}$ $8\overline{)24}$ $7\overline{)7}$

C. $2\overline{)16}$ $8\overline{)40}$ $8\overline{)16}$ $5\overline{)20}$ $4\overline{)28}$ $6\overline{)18}$

D. $8\overline{)64}$ $2\overline{)18}$ $8\overline{)56}$ $6\overline{)24}$ $6\overline{)54}$ $6\overline{)12}$

E. $5\overline{)30}$ $5\overline{)15}$ $4\overline{)8}$ $9\overline{)63}$ $8\overline{)40}$ $7\overline{)28}$

F. $9\overline{)54}$ $9\overline{)36}$ $1\overline{)9}$ $5\overline{)0}$ $6\overline{)30}$ $6\overline{)48}$

G. $7\overline{)49}$ $5\overline{)40}$ $8\overline{)64}$ $2\overline{)2}$ $2\overline{)10}$ $4\overline{)20}$

H. $4\overline{)24}$ $4\overline{)28}$ $5\overline{)45}$ $3\overline{)24}$ $6\overline{)24}$ $5\overline{)30}$

    Ten Divided by Five Is Not Five: Using Multiplication to Make Division Easy

SECTION 5

Name _____

Cumulative Division Practice. Review the division facts.

A. $9 \div 9 =$ ___ $12 \div 4 =$ ___ $14 \div 7 =$ ___ $30 \div 6 =$ ___ $40 \div 5 =$ ___

B. $24 \div 8 =$ ___ $18 \div 3 =$ ___ $28 \div 4 =$ ___ $24 \div 6 =$ ___ $54 \div 9 =$ ___

C. $49 \div 7 =$ ___ $6 \div 2 =$ ___ $6 \div 1 =$ ___ $28 \div 7 =$ ___ $45 \div 5 =$ ___

D. $24 \div 6 =$ ___ $40 \div 5 =$ ___ $8 \div 2 =$ ___ $40 \div 8 =$ ___ $30 \div 5 =$ ___

E. $64 \div 8 =$ ___ $56 \div 7 =$ ___ $12 \div 2 =$ ___ $30 \div 6 =$ ___ $81 \div 9 =$ ___

F. $48 \div 8 =$ ___ $49 \div 7 =$ ___ $7 \div 1 =$ ___ $24 \div 4 =$ ___ $45 \div 9 =$ ___

G. $6 \div 6 =$ ___ $25 \div 5 =$ ___ $9 \div 3 =$ ___ $18 \div 9 =$ ___ $28 \div 7 =$ ___

H. $20 \div 5 =$ ___ $16 \div 4 =$ ___ $64 \div 8 =$ ___ $24 \div 3 =$ ___ $63 \div 7 =$ ___

I. $28 \div 4 =$ ___ $54 \div 6 =$ ___ $10 \div 5 =$ ___ $6 \div 3 =$ ___ $40 \div 8 =$ ___

J. $15 \div 3 =$ ___ $24 \div 4 =$ ___ $30 \div 5 =$ ___ $36 \div 6 =$ ___ $20 \div 4 =$ ___

40   Ten Divided by Five Is Not Five: Using Multiplication to Make Division Easy

Name _____

Multiply.

A.	9 × 8	3 × 5	7 × 5	2 × 3	7 × 3	7 × 6	9 × 4

A.
$\begin{array}{r}9\\\times 8\end{array}$ $\begin{array}{r}3\\\times 5\end{array}$ $\begin{array}{r}7\\\times 5\end{array}$ $\begin{array}{r}2\\\times 3\end{array}$ $\begin{array}{r}7\\\times 3\end{array}$ $\begin{array}{r}7\\\times 6\end{array}$ $\begin{array}{r}9\\\times 4\end{array}$

B.
$\begin{array}{r}4\\\times 4\end{array}$ $\begin{array}{r}3\\\times 9\end{array}$ $\begin{array}{r}8\\\times 4\end{array}$ $\begin{array}{r}4\\\times 8\end{array}$ $\begin{array}{r}6\\\times 5\end{array}$ $\begin{array}{r}8\\\times 5\end{array}$ $\begin{array}{r}9\\\times 9\end{array}$

C.
$\begin{array}{r}7\\\times 8\end{array}$ $\begin{array}{r}4\\\times 2\end{array}$ $\begin{array}{r}8\\\times 9\end{array}$ $\begin{array}{r}6\\\times 7\end{array}$ $\begin{array}{r}3\\\times 4\end{array}$ $\begin{array}{r}3\\\times 7\end{array}$ $\begin{array}{r}9\\\times 3\end{array}$

D.
$\begin{array}{r}5\\\times 6\end{array}$ $\begin{array}{r}6\\\times 8\end{array}$ $\begin{array}{r}7\\\times 3\end{array}$ $\begin{array}{r}7\\\times 4\end{array}$ $\begin{array}{r}5\\\times 9\end{array}$ $\begin{array}{r}8\\\times 8\end{array}$ $\begin{array}{r}5\\\times 7\end{array}$

E.
$\begin{array}{r}4\\\times 6\end{array}$ $\begin{array}{r}8\\\times 4\end{array}$ $\begin{array}{r}9\\\times 7\end{array}$ $\begin{array}{r}7\\\times 1\end{array}$ $\begin{array}{r}3\\\times 8\end{array}$ $\begin{array}{r}9\\\times 6\end{array}$ $\begin{array}{r}3\\\times 7\end{array}$

F.
$\begin{array}{r}4\\\times 5\end{array}$ $\begin{array}{r}7\\\times 5\end{array}$ $\begin{array}{r}9\\\times 3\end{array}$ $\begin{array}{r}4\\\times 8\end{array}$ $\begin{array}{r}9\\\times 8\end{array}$ $\begin{array}{r}6\\\times 7\end{array}$ $\begin{array}{r}4\\\times 1\end{array}$

G.
$\begin{array}{r}0\\\times 0\end{array}$ $\begin{array}{r}4\\\times 7\end{array}$ $\begin{array}{r}5\\\times 8\end{array}$ $\begin{array}{r}2\\\times 6\end{array}$ $\begin{array}{r}5\\\times 7\end{array}$ $\begin{array}{r}3\\\times 6\end{array}$ $\begin{array}{r}7\\\times 6\end{array}$

H.
$\begin{array}{r}8\\\times 3\end{array}$ $\begin{array}{r}7\\\times 7\end{array}$ $\begin{array}{r}9\\\times 2\end{array}$ $\begin{array}{r}8\\\times 9\end{array}$ $\begin{array}{r}5\\\times 4\end{array}$ $\begin{array}{r}3\\\times 9\end{array}$ $\begin{array}{r}6\\\times 4\end{array}$

SECTION 6

Ten Divided by Five Is Not Five: Using Multiplication to Make Division Easy

Name _____

Find the missing factor.

A. $9 \times \underline{} = 81$ $3 \times \underline{} = 15$ $7 \times \underline{} = 35$ $8 \times \underline{} = 24$

B. $6 \times \underline{} = 42$ $\underline{} \times 7 = 21$ $\underline{} \times 3 = 27$ $7 \times \underline{} = 14$

C. $8 \times \underline{} = 40$ $4 \times \underline{} = 12$ $8 \times \underline{} = 32$ $\underline{} \times 4 = 28$

D. $8 \times \underline{} = 72$ $8 \times \underline{} = 56$ $\underline{} \times 6 = 30$ $2 \times \underline{} = 2$

E. $9 \times \underline{} = 27$ $4 \times \underline{} = 24$ $8 \times \underline{} = 48$ $\underline{} \times 7 = 35$

F. $\underline{} \times 7 = 42$ $2 \times \underline{} = 16$ $7 \times \underline{} = 21$ $9 \times \underline{} = 36$

G. $3 \times \underline{} = 0$ $5 \times \underline{} = 20$ $4 \times \underline{} = 16$ $9 \times \underline{} = 54$

H. $6 \times \underline{} = 18$ $\underline{} \times 8 = 32$ $1 \times \underline{} = 9$ $7 \times \underline{} = 49$

I. $\underline{} \times 9 = 45$ $7 \times \underline{} = 63$ $2 \times \underline{} = 12$ $\underline{} \times 9 = 72$

  Ten Divided by Five Is Not Five: Using Multiplication to Make Division Easy

Name _____

Solve the problems.

A. There are 18 boys on Christian's baseball team. Last month, 9 of them bought tickets to go to a movie. If the total cost was $72 for the tickets, how much was each ticket?

Answer: _____

B. Find the area of a clothes closet that is 9 feet long and 3 feet wide.

Answer: _____

C. Julia has to read 4 pages each day. She has 6 detective story books. How long will it take her to read 32 pages?

Answer: _____

D. William opened a bag of peppermint candy and put 5 pieces in each of the 9 party bags. If the peppermint candy bag has 3 pieces left, how many candies were there in all?

Answer: _____

E. A rancher has many fenced-off areas for 6 different animals. He has 42 cows and wants to keep 7 cows in each fenced area. How many areas will he need for the cows?

Answer: _____

F. Ashley's grandma gave her $27. Ashley plans to take equal amounts to save some money, spend some money, and donate to the local soup kitchen. In all, how much money will she spend and donate?

Answer: _____

Name _____

Divide.

A. $72 \div 8 = $___ $42 \div$___$= 7$ $36 \div 6 = $___ $49 \div 7 = $___ $27 \div 9 = $___

B. $18 \div 6 = $___ $21 \div 7 = $___ $32 \div 8 = $___ $56 \div 8 = $___ $35 \div$___$= 5$

C. $24 \div 6 = $___ $8 \div 2 = $___ $28 \div 7 = $___ $30 \div 6 = $___ $54 \div 6 = $___

D. $28 \div$___$= 7$ $40 \div 5 = $___ $27 \div 3 = $___ $30 \div$___$= 6$ $12 \div 3 = $___

E. $21 \div 3 = $___ $64 \div 8 = $___ $72 \div 9 = $___ $35 \div 5 = $___ $45 \div 5 = $___

F. $42 \div 7 = $___ $35 \div 7 = $___ $24 \div 6 = $___ $8 \div 1 = $___ $32 \div 4 = $___

G. $3 \div 3 = $___ $32 \div 8 = $___ $21 \div$___$= 3$ $20 \div 5 = $___ $42 \div 6 = $___

H. $27 \div$___$= 9$ $21 \div 7 = $___ $48 \div 6 = $___ $35 \div 7 = $___ $72 \div$___$= 9$

I. $32 \div 4 = $___ $27 \div 9 = $___ $15 \div 5 = $___ $40 \div 8 = $___ $21 \div 3 = $___

J. $72 \div 9 = $___ $32 \div$___$= 8$ $24 \div 3 = $___ $42 \div 7 = $___ $35 \div 5 = $___

Ten Divided by Five Is Not Five: Using Multiplication to Make Division Easy

Name _____

Divide.

A. $7\overline{)21}$ $8\overline{)32}$ $6\overline{)30}$ $2\overline{)12}$ $8\overline{)72}$ $3\overline{)21}$

B. $8\overline{)64}$ $1\overline{)5}$ $9\overline{)27}$ $6\overline{)42}$ $5\overline{)40}$ $4\overline{)32}$

C. $8\overline{)24}$ $7\overline{)42}$ $5\overline{)35}$ $3\overline{)6}$ $3\overline{)27}$ $7\overline{)14}$

D. $4\overline{)36}$ $7\overline{)35}$ $4\overline{)28}$ $6\overline{)36}$ $9\overline{)27}$ $9\overline{)72}$

E. $3\overline{)27}$ $3\overline{)15}$ $7\overline{)21}$ $9\overline{)18}$ $7\overline{)56}$ $3\overline{)21}$

F. $7\overline{)42}$ $5\overline{)35}$ $5\overline{)10}$ $6\overline{)42}$ $4\overline{)32}$ $7\overline{)49}$

G. $8\overline{)32}$ $9\overline{)54}$ $8\overline{)72}$ $9\overline{)72}$ $7\overline{)28}$ $8\overline{)40}$

H. $5\overline{)30}$ $3\overline{)27}$ $7\overline{)42}$ $7\overline{)35}$ $7\overline{)21}$ $4\overline{)24}$

Ten Divided by Five Is Not Five: Using Multiplication to Make Division Easy   **45**

Name _____

Divide and multiply.

A. $12 \div 6 =$ ___ $36 \div 9 =$ ___ $5 \times 7 =$ ___ $35 \div 5 =$ ___ $32 \div 8 =$ ___

B. $30 \div 5 =$ ___ $6 \times 7 =$ ___ $42 \div 6 =$ ___ $20 \div 5 =$ ___ $6 \times 5 =$ ___

C. $4 \times 8 =$ ___ $24 \div 4 =$ ___ $4 \times 7 =$ ___ $40 \div 5 =$ ___ $72 \div 9 =$ ___

D. $21 \div 7 =$ ___ $9 \times 4 =$ ___ $56 \div 7 =$ ___ $42 \div 7 =$ ___ $3 \times 7 =$ ___

E. $9 \times 8 =$ ___ $18 \div 2 =$ ___ $35 \div 7 =$ ___ $27 \div 3 =$ ___ $30 \div 5 =$ ___

F. $32 \div 4 =$ ___ $3 \times 9 =$ ___ $24 \div 8 =$ ___ $7 \times 6 =$ ___ $18 \div 3 =$ ___

G. $28 \div 7 =$ ___ $45 \div 5 =$ ___ $8 \times 8 =$ ___ $64 \div 8 =$ ___ $30 \div 6 =$ ___

H. $8 \times 6 =$ ___ $27 \div 9 =$ ___ $1 \times 5 =$ ___ $8 \times 4 =$ ___ $6 \div 2 =$ ___

I. $21 \div 3 =$ ___ $28 \div 4 =$ ___ $72 \div 8 =$ ___ $24 \div 6 =$ ___ $7 \times 3 =$ ___

J. $63 \div 7 =$ ___ $40 \div 8 =$ ___ $49 \div 7 =$ ___ $8 \times 9 =$ ___ $25 \div 5 =$ ___

Ten Divided by Five Is Not Five: Using Multiplication to Make Division Easy

Name _____

Divide.

A. $9\overline{)72}$ $7\overline{)21}$ $8\overline{)40}$ $3\overline{)27}$ $4\overline{)32}$ $4\overline{)12}$

B. $6\overline{)42}$ $3\overline{)24}$ $8\overline{)64}$ $6\overline{)0}$ $3\overline{)21}$ $8\overline{)72}$

C. $6\overline{)24}$ $7\overline{)35}$ $4\overline{)4}$ $8\overline{)32}$ $7\overline{)42}$ $9\overline{)27}$

D. $9\overline{)63}$ $3\overline{)27}$ $5\overline{)35}$ $9\overline{)72}$ $4\overline{)28}$ $3\overline{)9}$

E. $5\overline{)35}$ $6\overline{)54}$ $8\overline{)72}$ $6\overline{)42}$ $6\overline{)30}$ $7\overline{)21}$

F. $8\overline{)48}$ $6\overline{)18}$ $9\overline{)45}$ $7\overline{)42}$ $8\overline{)32}$ $9\overline{)72}$

G. $4\overline{)16}$ $4\overline{)20}$ $4\overline{)32}$ $9\overline{)27}$ $1\overline{)7}$ $3\overline{)21}$

H. $7\overline{)49}$ $5\overline{)40}$ $7\overline{)35}$ $3\overline{)21}$ $5\overline{)30}$ $7\overline{)28}$

Ten Divided by Five Is Not Five: Using Multiplication to Make Division Easy

Name _____

Divide.

A. $27 \div 3 =$ ___ $35 \div$ ___ $= 7$ $2 \div 2 =$ ___ $30 \div 6 =$ ___ $81 \div 9 =$ ___

B. $72 \div 9 =$ ___ $0 \div 1 =$ ___ $16 \div 8 =$ ___ $48 \div 8 =$ ___ $10 \div$ ___ $= 5$

C. $6 \div 3 =$ ___ $32 \div 8 =$ ___ $36 \div 4 =$ ___ $21 \div 7 =$ ___ $18 \div 9 =$ ___

D. $42 \div$ ___ $= 6$ $4 \div 1 =$ ___ $36 \div 6 =$ ___ $40 \div$ ___ $= 8$ $20 \div 5 =$ ___

E. $16 \div 2 =$ ___ $45 \div 9 =$ ___ $27 \div 9 =$ ___ $35 \div 7 =$ ___ $63 \div 9 =$ ___

F. $48 \div 6 =$ ___ $54 \div 9 =$ ___ $32 \div 4 =$ ___ $3 \div 1 =$ ___ $56 \div 8 =$ ___

G. $12 \div 4 =$ ___ $40 \div 8 =$ ___ $24 \div$ ___ $= 6$ $28 \div 7 =$ ___ $24 \div 8 =$ ___

H. $8 \div$ ___ $= 2$ $72 \div 8 =$ ___ $30 \div 5 =$ ___ $20 \div 4 =$ ___ $15 \div$ ___ $= 5$

I. $14 \div 2 =$ ___ $36 \div 9 =$ ___ $42 \div 6 =$ ___ $24 \div 3 =$ ___ $45 \div 5 =$ ___

J. $24 \div 6 =$ ___ $7 \div$ ___ $= 1$ $21 \div 3 =$ ___ $4 \div 2 =$ ___ $28 \div 4 =$ ___

Ten Divided by Five Is Not Five: Using Multiplication to Make Division Easy

Name _____

Divide.

A. $7\overline{)35}$ $3\overline{)21}$ $3\overline{)27}$ $8\overline{)72}$ $6\overline{)24}$ $7\overline{)28}$

B. $5\overline{)15}$ $5\overline{)30}$ $4\overline{)32}$ $7\overline{)42}$ $5\overline{)35}$ $8\overline{)32}$

C. $6\overline{)42}$ $8\overline{)72}$ $8\overline{)64}$ $3\overline{)21}$ $6\overline{)54}$ $9\overline{)72}$

D. $3\overline{)27}$ $3\overline{)18}$ $7\overline{)35}$ $9\overline{)27}$ $6\overline{)42}$ $7\overline{)49}$

E. $9\overline{)72}$ $8\overline{)32}$ $9\overline{)45}$ $5\overline{)35}$ $7\overline{)21}$ $8\overline{)40}$

F. $7\overline{)21}$ $7\overline{)42}$ $4\overline{)32}$ $6\overline{)30}$ $4\overline{)24}$ $3\overline{)21}$

G. $8\overline{)32}$ $7\overline{)63}$ $3\overline{)27}$ $5\overline{)40}$ $9\overline{)72}$ $7\overline{)35}$

H. $4\overline{)28}$ $5\overline{)20}$ $4\overline{)32}$ $8\overline{)72}$ $9\overline{)27}$ $6\overline{)42}$

    Ten Divided by Five Is Not Five: Using Multiplication to Make Division Easy

Name _____

Divide.

A. $32 \div 8 =$ ___ $30 \div 5 =$ ___ $42 \div 7 =$ ___ $72 \div 9 =$ ___ $27 \div 9 =$ ___

B. $40 \div 8 =$ ___ $21 \div 7 =$ ___ $28 \div 7 =$ ___ $24 \div 6 =$ ___ $35 \div 5 =$ ___

C. $32 \div 4 =$ ___ $42 \div 6 =$ ___ $27 \div 3 =$ ___ $21 \div 3 =$ ___ $20 \div 4 =$ ___

D. $35 \div 7 =$ ___ $72 \div 8 =$ ___ $12 \div 6 =$ ___ $35 \div 5 =$ ___ $72 \div 9 =$ ___

E. $21 \div 3 =$ ___ $27 \div 9 =$ ___ $42 \div 6 =$ ___ $30 \div 6 =$ ___ $27 \div 3 =$ ___

F. $32 \div 8 =$ ___ $40 \div 5 =$ ___ $35 \div 7 =$ ___ $49 \div 7 =$ ___ $21 \div 7 =$ ___

G. $9 \div 1 =$ ___ $32 \div 4 =$ ___ $42 \div 7 =$ ___ $72 \div 8 =$ ___ $28 \div 4 =$ ___

H. $27 \div 9 =$ ___ $21 \div 3 =$ ___ $72 \div 9 =$ ___ $42 \div 6 =$ ___ $24 \div 4 =$ ___

I. $32 \div 4 =$ ___ $72 \div 8 =$ ___ $27 \div 3 =$ ___ $35 \div 7 =$ ___ $15 \div 5 =$ ___

J. $35 \div 5 =$ ___ $21 \div 7 =$ ___ $64 \div 8 =$ ___ $32 \div 8 =$ ___ $42 \div 7 =$ ___

Ten Divided by Five Is Not Five: Using Multiplication to Make Division Easy

Name _____

Divide.

A. $8\overline{)64}$ $7\overline{)35}$ $8\overline{)56}$ $6\overline{)48}$ $7\overline{)28}$ $3\overline{)24}$

B. $8\overline{)32}$ $1\overline{)2}$ $6\overline{)42}$ $3\overline{)27}$ $5\overline{)25}$ $3\overline{)21}$

C. $2\overline{)6}$ $7\overline{)42}$ $7\overline{)63}$ $5\overline{)40}$ $6\overline{)6}$ $3\overline{)12}$

D. $7\overline{)21}$ $9\overline{)27}$ $2\overline{)10}$ $4\overline{)32}$ $5\overline{)20}$ $8\overline{)32}$

E. $2\overline{)0}$ $8\overline{)72}$ $3\overline{)15}$ $6\overline{)30}$ $9\overline{)72}$ $4\overline{)32}$

F. $9\overline{)81}$ $8\overline{)16}$ $5\overline{)35}$ $7\overline{)21}$ $6\overline{)42}$ $4\overline{)36}$

G. $9\overline{)9}$ $5\overline{)45}$ $8\overline{)72}$ $6\overline{)24}$ $7\overline{)35}$ $9\overline{)54}$

H. $5\overline{)35}$ $9\overline{)27}$ $7\overline{)42}$ $9\overline{)72}$ $3\overline{)21}$ $3\overline{)27}$

Ten Divided by Five Is Not Five: Using Multiplication to Make Division Easy

SECTION 6

Name _____

Solve the problems.

A. Eve and Madison each had 16 princess stickers. The girls put
    8 stickers on each sticker book page. How many pages did they
    use together?

Answer: _____
_____

B. Michael ordered 40 boxes of fresh vegetables for his restaurant.
    The delivery truck piled them in stacks of 5 boxes high. How many
    stacks of vegetables were there in all? How much did each stack
    weigh if each box weighed 4 pounds?

Answer: _____
_____

C. Every Friday, Charlotte's grade has a spelling contest. The two
    third-grade classes each have 21 students, and they are grouped
    in teams of 6. How many teams are there altogether?

Answer: _____
_____

D. Sweets Ice Cream store serves 27 different flavors of ice cream
    each day. On Tuesday, they had a sale, and cones were $2. They
    ran out of 9 flavors. How many flavors were still there to choose
    from?

Answer: _____
_____

E. Jordan had $20 to spend on school supplies. He wants to buy
    1 box of crayons for $2, 5 notebooks for $3 each, a ruler for $1,
    and 3 packages of pencils for $4 each. How much more money
    does he need?

Answer: _____
_____

F. Each round table in Allison's classroom has room for 7 students.
    Each table in Jessica's classroom has room for 3 students. If
    Jessica's class has 21 students and Allison's class has 35, how
    many more tables does Jessica's classroom need than Allison's?

Answer: _____

Ten Divided by Five Is Not Five: Using Multiplication to Make Division Easy

Name _____

Divide.

A. $3\overline{)3}$ $7\overline{)49}$ $9\overline{)27}$ $6\overline{)12}$ $7\overline{)35}$ $7\overline{)21}$

B. $9\overline{)27}$ $7\overline{)28}$ $5\overline{)30}$ $9\overline{)72}$ $8\overline{)32}$ $7\overline{)56}$

C. $8\overline{)72}$ $3\overline{)21}$ $2\overline{)8}$ $6\overline{)42}$ $4\overline{)16}$ $4\overline{)20}$

D. $4\overline{)32}$ $4\overline{)24}$ $5\overline{)35}$ $3\overline{)27}$ $4\overline{)28}$ $8\overline{)0}$

E. $7\overline{)42}$ $9\overline{)63}$ $1\overline{)6}$ $8\overline{)48}$ $3\overline{)21}$ $6\overline{)54}$

F. $5\overline{)35}$ $6\overline{)36}$ $8\overline{)32}$ $9\overline{)72}$ $3\overline{)18}$ $8\overline{)72}$

G. $8\overline{)40}$ $7\overline{)42}$ $2\overline{)4}$ $3\overline{)27}$ $6\overline{)42}$ $4\overline{)32}$

H. $4\overline{)12}$ $7\overline{)21}$ $9\overline{)36}$ $5\overline{)45}$ $5\overline{)10}$ $7\overline{)35}$

Ten Divided by Five Is Not Five: Using Multiplication to Make Division Easy

Name _____

Divide.

A. $24 \div 4 =$ ___ $40 \div 8 =$ ___ $72 \div 8 =$ ___ $35 \div 5 =$ ___ $48 \div 8 =$ ___

B. $18 \div 6 =$ ___ $42 \div 6 =$ ___ $27 \div 3 =$ ___ $32 \div 8 =$ ___ $0 \div 7 =$ ___

C. $5 \div 1 =$ ___ $21 \div 3 =$ ___ $14 \div 7 =$ ___ $45 \div 9 =$ ___ $18 \div 2 =$ ___

D. $24 \div 8 =$ ___ $49 \div 7 =$ ___ $30 \div 5 =$ ___ $27 \div 9 =$ ___ $42 \div 7 =$ ___

E. $32 \div 4 =$ ___ $35 \div 7 =$ ___ $36 \div 9 =$ ___ $21 \div 3 =$ ___ $9 \div 3 =$ ___

F. $27 \div 9 =$ ___ $72 \div 8 =$ ___ $42 \div 6 =$ ___ $56 \div 7 =$ ___ $32 \div 4 =$ ___

G. $72 \div 9 =$ ___ $21 \div 7 =$ ___ $12 \div 2 =$ ___ $5 \div 5 =$ ___ $27 \div 3 =$ ___

H. $42 \div 7 =$ ___ $32 \div 8 =$ ___ $16 \div 4 =$ ___ $72 \div 9 =$ ___ $8 \div 4 =$ ___

I. $35 \div 5 =$ ___ $27 \div 3 =$ ___ $12 \div 3 =$ ___ $42 \div 6 =$ ___ $72 \div 8 =$ ___

J. $21 \div 7 =$ ___ $54 \div 6 =$ ___ $63 \div 9 =$ ___ $28 \div 4 =$ ___ $35 \div 7 =$ ___

Ten Divided by Five Is Not Five: Using Multiplication to Make Division Easy

Name _____

Divide.

A. $5\overline{)35}$ $9\overline{)72}$ $5\overline{)40}$ $4\overline{)32}$ $1\overline{)1}$ $7\overline{)42}$

B. $3\overline{)24}$ $2\overline{)16}$ $9\overline{)27}$ $9\overline{)54}$ $7\overline{)63}$ $3\overline{)21}$

C. $4\overline{)20}$ $7\overline{)21}$ $3\overline{)15}$ $8\overline{)32}$ $6\overline{)24}$ $8\overline{)72}$

D. $9\overline{)63}$ $7\overline{)42}$ $2\overline{)6}$ $7\overline{)35}$ $3\overline{)27}$ $9\overline{)18}$

E. $4\overline{)36}$ $2\overline{)14}$ $3\overline{)21}$ $7\overline{)0}$ $8\overline{)24}$ $6\overline{)42}$

F. $6\overline{)30}$ $1\overline{)8}$ $8\overline{)72}$ $5\overline{)15}$ $4\overline{)32}$ $5\overline{)35}$

G. $6\overline{)42}$ $7\overline{)35}$ $8\overline{)32}$ $8\overline{)16}$ $5\overline{)45}$ $9\overline{)27}$

H. $9\overline{)72}$ $6\overline{)48}$ $3\overline{)27}$ $9\overline{)9}$ $7\overline{)21}$ $3\overline{)6}$

SECTION 6

    Ten Divided by Five Is Not Five: Using Multiplication to Make Division Easy   **55**

Name _____

Divide.

A. $72 \div 8 =$ ___ $35 \div 7 =$ ___ $21 \div 3 =$ ___ $28 \div 4 =$ ___ $54 \div 9 =$ ___

B. $63 \div 7 =$ ___ $27 \div 3 =$ ___ $6 \div 3 =$ ___ $24 \div 3 =$ ___ $32 \div 4 =$ ___

C. $42 \div 7 =$ ___ $30 \div 6 =$ ___ $27 \div 9 =$ ___ $36 \div 4 =$ ___ $35 \div 5 =$ ___

D. $72 \div 9 =$ ___ $49 \div 7 =$ ___ $7 \div 7 =$ ___ $42 \div 6 =$ ___ $24 \div 6 =$ ___

E. $14 \div 7 =$ ___ $24 \div 4 =$ ___ $21 \div 7 =$ ___ $14 \div 2 =$ ___ $32 \div 8 =$ ___

F. $81 \div 9 =$ ___ $21 \div 3 =$ ___ $35 \div 5 =$ ___ $72 \div 9 =$ ___ $27 \div 9 =$ ___

G. $20 \div 5 =$ ___ $0 \div 1 =$ ___ $64 \div 8 =$ ___ $21 \div 7 =$ ___ $24 \div 8 =$ ___

H. $40 \div 8 =$ ___ $48 \div 6 =$ ___ $32 \div 4 =$ ___ $27 \div 3 =$ ___ $72 \div 8 =$ ___

I. $30 \div 5 =$ ___ $63 \div 9 =$ ___ $15 \div 3 =$ ___ $8 \div 1 =$ ___ $42 \div 7 =$ ___

J. $45 \div 9 =$ ___ $35 \div 7 =$ ___ $32 \div 8 =$ ___ $42 \div 6 =$ ___ $54 \div 6 =$ ___

Ten Divided by Five Is Not Five: Using Multiplication to Make Division Easy

Name _____

Cumulative Division Practice. Review the division facts.

A. $9\overline{)45}$ $3\overline{)27}$ $9\overline{)36}$ $5\overline{)0}$ $4\overline{)24}$ $5\overline{)35}$

B. $8\overline{)56}$ $1\overline{)9}$ $8\overline{)32}$ $6\overline{)42}$ $2\overline{)8}$ $6\overline{)30}$

C. $5\overline{)5}$ $5\overline{)15}$ $9\overline{)72}$ $7\overline{)21}$ $7\overline{)49}$ $3\overline{)24}$

D. $2\overline{)18}$ $3\overline{)9}$ $8\overline{)48}$ $2\overline{)12}$ $8\overline{)40}$ $9\overline{)54}$

E. $5\overline{)20}$ $3\overline{)6}$ $2\overline{)2}$ $9\overline{)27}$ $9\overline{)81}$ $6\overline{)24}$

F. $3\overline{)12}$ $7\overline{)63}$ $6\overline{)0}$ $5\overline{)30}$ $4\overline{)16}$ $7\overline{)7}$

G. $4\overline{)28}$ $7\overline{)35}$ $5\overline{)40}$ $7\overline{)42}$ $1\overline{)5}$ $8\overline{)64}$

H. $7\overline{)14}$ $3\overline{)3}$ $1\overline{)3}$ $5\overline{)25}$ $7\overline{)28}$ $4\overline{)32}$

Ten Divided by Five Is Not Five: Using Multiplication to Make Division Easy

SECTION 6

Name _____

Cumulative Division Practice. Review the division facts.

A. $2 \div 1 =$ ___ $21 \div 7 =$ ___ $64 \div 8 =$ ___ $18 \div 9 =$ ___ $27 \div 9 =$ ___

B. $56 \div 7 =$ ___ $4 \div 1 =$ ___ $16 \div 2 =$ ___ $42 \div 6 =$ ___ $20 \div 4 =$ ___

C. $10 \div 5 =$ ___ $32 \div 8 =$ ___ $1 \div 1 =$ ___ $72 \div 9 =$ ___ $48 \div 6 =$ ___

D. $4 \div 4 =$ ___ $4 \div 2 =$ ___ $15 \div 3 =$ ___ $63 \div 9 =$ ___ $7 \div 1 =$ ___

E. $28 \div 7 =$ ___ $12 \div 4 =$ ___ $5 \div 1 =$ ___ $0 \div 4 =$ ___ $40 \div 5 =$ ___

F. $15 \div 5 =$ ___ $36 \div 4 =$ ___ $14 \div 2 =$ ___ $8 \div 8 =$ ___ $45 \div 5 =$ ___

G. $6 \div 2 =$ ___ $30 \div 6 =$ ___ $42 \div 7 =$ ___ $18 \div 3 =$ ___ $24 \div 4 =$ ___

H. $12 \div 6 =$ ___ $10 \div 2 =$ ___ $18 \div 2 =$ ___ $8 \div 1 =$ ___ $8 \div 2 =$ ___

I. $24 \div 8 =$ ___ $54 \div 6 =$ ___ $35 \div 5 =$ ___ $56 \div 8 =$ ___ $16 \div 8 =$ ___

J. $72 \div 8 =$ ___ $36 \div 6 =$ ___ $8 \div 4 =$ ___ $36 \div 9 =$ ___ $21 \div 3 =$ ___

Ten Divided by Five Is Not Five: Using Multiplication to Make Division Easy

Name _____

Pre-Assessment

A. $8\overline{)72}$ $4\overline{)20}$ $2\overline{)6}$ $9\overline{)27}$ $4\overline{)28}$ $7\overline{)21}$

B. $8\overline{)8}$ $2\overline{)16}$ $8\overline{)24}$ $1\overline{)7}$ $6\overline{)54}$ $3\overline{)15}$

C. $3\overline{)18}$ $6\overline{)48}$ $4\overline{)0}$ $6\overline{)30}$ $9\overline{)18}$ $8\overline{)40}$

D. $4\overline{)32}$ $5\overline{)45}$ $7\overline{)56}$ $9\overline{)63}$ $2\overline{)10}$ $1\overline{)2}$

E. $63 \div 7 =$ ___ $6 \div 6 =$ ___ $35 \div 7 =$ ___ $20 \div 5 =$ ___ $36 \div 6 =$ ___

F. $21 \div 3 =$ ___ $42 \div 6 =$ ___ $9 \div 1 =$ ___ $16 \div 8 =$ ___ $27 \div 3 =$ ___

G. $28 \div 7 =$ ___ $24 \div 3 =$ ___ $12 \div 6 =$ ___ $18 \div 2 =$ ___ $40 \div 5 =$ ___

H. $3 \div 1 =$ ___ $8 \div 2 =$ ___ $48 \div 8 =$ ___ $24 \div 6 =$ ___ $45 \div 9 =$ ___

I. $49 \div 7 =$ ___ $72 \div 9 =$ ___ $16 \div 4 =$ ___ $5 \div 5 =$ ___ $36 \div 4 =$ ___

J. $32 \div 8 =$ ___ $14 \div 7 =$ ___ $0 \div 7 =$ ___ $10 \div 5 =$ ___ $12 \div 3 =$ ___

   Ten Divided by Five Is Not Five: Using Multiplication to Make Division Easy   **59**

Name _____

Post-Assessment

A. $2\overline{)14}$ $4\overline{)36}$ $4\overline{)12}$ $5\overline{)10}$ $7\overline{)49}$ $1\overline{)6}$

B. $5\overline{)40}$ $9\overline{)0}$ $6\overline{)42}$ $3\overline{)27}$ $6\overline{)12}$ $9\overline{)72}$

C. $9\overline{)45}$ $8\overline{)16}$ $1\overline{)1}$ $8\overline{)32}$ $7\overline{)35}$ $4\overline{)8}$

D. $3\overline{)21}$ $6\overline{)24}$ $2\overline{)4}$ $3\overline{)24}$ $1\overline{)8}$ $7\overline{)63}$

E. $9 \div 3 = $___ $28 \div 4 = $___ $6 \div 3 = $___ $32 \div 4 = $___ $9 \div 9 = $___

F. $48 \div 6 = $___ $56 \div 8 = $___ $21 \div 7 = $___ $64 \div 8 = $___ $25 \div 5 = $___

G. $12 \div 2 = $___ $5 \div 1 = $___ $15 \div 5 = $___ $72 \div 8 = $___ $54 \div 9 = $___

H. $63 \div 9 = $___ $24 \div 4 = $___ $20 \div 4 = $___ $0 \div 2 = $___ $27 \div 9 = $___

I. $45 \div 5 = $___ $40 \div 8 = $___ $16 \div 2 = $___ $81 \div 9 = $___ $36 \div 9 = $___

J. $42 \div 7 = $___ $18 \div 6 = $___ $2 \div 2 = $___ $35 \div 5 = $___ $30 \div 5 = $___

Ten Divided by Five Is Not Five: Using Multiplication to Make Division Easy

Math Facts Baseline Recorder

Division

Name _____

Baseline Date _____   Division Facts: + _____ / 81

Circle KNOWN facts.   Check KNOWN concept of Zero.

81 Division Facts

Concept of Zero: (Zero ÷ Number) _____

1÷1	2÷1	3÷1	4÷1	5÷1	6÷1	7÷1	8÷1	9÷1
2÷2	4÷2	6÷2	8÷2	10÷2	12÷2	14÷2	16÷2	18÷2
3÷3	6÷3	9÷3	12÷3	15÷3	18÷3	21÷3	24÷3	27÷3
4÷4	8÷4	12÷4	16÷4	20÷4	24÷4	28÷4	32÷4	36÷4
5÷5	10÷5	15÷5	20÷5	25÷5	30÷5	35÷5	40÷5	45÷5
6÷6	12÷6	18÷6	24÷6	30÷6	36÷6	42÷6	48÷6	54÷6
7÷7	14÷7	21÷7	28÷7	35÷7	42÷7	49÷7	56÷7	63÷7
8÷8	16÷8	24÷8	32÷8	40÷8	48÷8	56÷8	64÷8	72÷8
9÷9	18÷9	27÷9	36÷9	45÷9	54÷9	63÷9	72÷9	81÷9

Ten Divided by Five Is Not Five: Using Multiplication to Make Division Easy

Record-Keeping Checklist

Notes	Section Page	Facts Covered in Each Section

Section 1　　Page 1

_____

_____

_____

_____

_____

_____

_____

$1÷1$	$2÷2$	$3÷3$	$4÷4$	$5÷5$	$6÷6$	$7÷7$	$8÷8$	$9÷9$
	$2÷1$	$3÷1$	$4÷1$	$5÷1$	$6÷1$	$7÷1$	$8÷1$	$9÷1$
$4÷2$	$6÷2$	$8÷2$	$10÷2$	$12÷2$	$14÷2$	$16÷2$	$18÷2$	
	$6÷3$	$8÷4$	$10÷5$	$12÷6$	$14÷7$	$16÷8$	$18÷9$	

$56÷7$　$56÷8$

$9÷3$

$Zero ÷ Number$

Section 2　　Page 7

_____

_____

_____

$12÷3$　$12÷4$

$18÷3$　$18÷6$

$16÷4$　　　$25÷5$　　　$81÷9$

Section 3　　Page 15

_____

_____

_____

_____

$36÷4$　$36÷9$　　　$63÷7$　$63÷9$

$48÷6$　$48÷8$

$15÷3$　$15÷5$

$36÷6$

Section 4　　Page 23

_____

_____

_____

$54÷6$　$54÷9$　　　$45÷5$　$45÷9$

$24÷3$　$24÷8$

$20÷4$　$20÷5$

Section 5　　Page 31

_____

_____

_____

$24÷4$　$24÷6$　　　$28÷4$　$28÷7$

$30÷5$　$30÷6$　　　$40÷5$　$40÷8$

$49÷7$　　　$64÷8$

Section 6　　Page 41

_____

_____

_____

_____

$35÷5$　$35÷7$

$32÷4$　$32÷8$

$21÷3$　$21÷7$　　　$42÷6$　$42÷7$

$27÷3$　$27÷9$　　　$72÷8$　$72÷9$

Name _____　　Baseline Date _____

　Ten Divided by Five Is Not Five: Using Multiplication to Make Division Easy

Congratulations

to _____

date _____

for Mastery
of Division
Math Facts

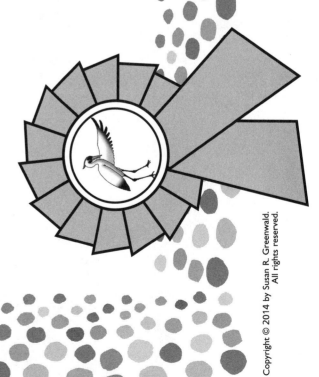

Answers

Page 1
A. 10, 8, 14, 1, 18, 4, 56
B. 5, 2, 0, 6, 8, 16, 9
C. 6, 12, 9, 18, 3, 4, 8
D. 10, 16, 12, 7, 56, 14, 6
E. 56, 4, 10, 9, 8, 12, 5
F. 6, 56, 8, 18, 7, 14, 16
G. 18, 10, 2, 0, 56, 9, 3
H. 4, 7, 16, 12, 8, 6, 6

Page 2
A. 2, 7, 8, 1
B. 7, 1, 7, 4
C. 2, 3, 2, 3
D. 7, 9, 8, 3
E. 1, 0, 8, 5
F. 2, 5, 2, 6
G. 6, 1, 1, 2
H. 2, 4, 9, 1
I. 2, 1, 1, 2

Page 3
A. 7 groups
B. 9 tables
C. 8 rows
D. $3 each
E. 2 shelves
F. No

Page 4
A. 7, 2, 4, 2, 3
B. 1, 2, 5, 0, 2
C. 8, 1, 1, 2, 1
D. 1, 7, 1, 3, 6
E. 3, 0, 8, 5, 8
F. 2, 4, 3, 1, 8
G. 2, 7, 3, 7, 0
H. 2, 1, 2, 9, 7
I. 2, 5, 1, 2, 8
J. 2, 8, 2, 3, 1

Page 5
A. 8, 4, 5, 8, 2, 2
B. 1, 3, 3, 1, 2, 2
C. 8, 2, 5, 1, 7, 2
D. 0, 2, 6, 2, 1, 9
E. 7, 2, 4, 8, 7, 1
F. 2, 3, 2, 6, 1, 3
G. 9, 3, 1, 6, 9, 1
H. 7, 2, 0, 4, 1, 2

Page 6
A. 6, 7, 6, 2, 2
B. 1, 12, 9, 4, 2
C. 9, 2, 8, 0, 3
D. 4, 4, 9, 8, 56
E. 5, 1, 2, 2, 3
F. 5, 10, 8, 16, 7
G. 7, 2, 56, 1, 7
H. 8, 2, 14, 18, 1
I. 2, 9, 1, 2, 0
J. 3, 1, 6, 9, 8

Page 7
A. 12, 56, 12, 10, 9, 18, 7
B. 25, 10, 6, 12, 16, 18, 8
C. 56, 81, 3, 14, 18, 9, 16
D. 16, 6, 18, 8, 12, 25, 18
E. 81, 14, 56, 8, 1, 3, 12
F. 5, 0, 18, 18, 4, 12, 56
G. 9, 6, 16, 6, 12, 81, 18
H. 12, 2, 25, 16, 4, 7, 4

Page 8
A. 2, 9, 3, 3
B. 7, 4, 3, 1
C. 5, 8, 2, 6
D. 4, 2, 1, 6
E. 2, 1, 2, 6
F. 7, 4, 2, 4
G. 3, 9, 2, 1
H. 8, 9, 2, 5
I. 4, 0, 6, 5

Page 9
A. 4 tables
B. 15 classrooms
C. $24
D. 5 desks
E. 9 boxes, 18 trucks
F. 3 girls

Page 10
A. 5, 2, 4, 3, 9
B. 1, 4, 6, 3, 5
C. 3, 9, 8, 2, 2
D. 7, 2, 6, 1, 2
E. 2, 1, 8, 5, 4
F. 3, 3, 5, 7, 4
G. 0, 1, 4, 5, 9
H. 4, 5, 1, 6, 3
I. 4, 0, 2, 1, 3
J. 1, 2, 3, 3, 8

Page 11
A. 5, 5, 7, 4, 2, 4
B. 6, 6, 1, 3, 9, 8
C. 2, 3, 1, 8, 1, 3
D. 2, 4, 2, 6, 4, 3
E. 2, 0, 5, 9, 7, 2
F. 1, 9, 3, 7, 4, 6
G. 3, 5, 2, 3, 3, 6
H. 5, 0, 4, 4, 9, 2

Page 12
A. 9, 2, 18, 2, 6
B. 3, 9, 7, 6, 0
C. 25, 3, 12, 1, 5
D. 7, 16, 2, 4, 56
E. 3, 0, 2, 4, 1
F. 8, 12, 2, 12, 2
G. 5, 5, 18, 8, 3
H. 81, 3, 14, 8, 1
I. 9, 2, 9, 3, 18
J. 4, 6, 4, 5, 4

Page 13
A. 1, 9, 7, 0, 7
B. 2, 3, 4, 2, 1
C. 1, 3, 2, 2, 6
D. 3, 1, 5, 6, 3
E. 4, 8, 0, 1, 9
F. 2, 4, 2, 2, 3
G. 7, 1, 3, 0, 1
H. 0, 6, 4, 1, 3
I. 2, 6, 8, 2, 5
J. 1, 9, 5, 4, 8

Page 14
A. 2, 9, 2, 7, 5, 3
B. 3, 3, 1, 2, 1, 2
C. 3, 2, 4, 8, 6, 9
D. 1, 0, 8, 2, 1, 4
E. 6, 9, 9, 7, 2
F. 1, 1, 3, 0, 4
G. 4, 7, 5, 4, 1
H. 5, 8, 4, 3, 1
I. 6, 6, 1, 8, 5
J. 2, 7, 2, 3, 2

Page 15
A. 36, 48, 14, 16, 36, 9, 18
B. 63, 4, 15, 16, 48, 12, 81
C. 6, 36, 7, 63, 18, 56, 10
D. 15, 25, 18, 12, 8, 4, 12
E. 81, 15, 18, 1, 63, 12, 0
F. 36, 16, 9, 6, 15, 56, 9
G. 48, 10, 8, 0, 36, 18, 63
H. 8, 12, 36, 48, 14, 3, 18

Page 16
A. 4, 6, 4, 5
B. 5, 2, 7, 8
C. 1, 9, 9, 6
D. 5, 3, 3, 7
E. 2, 7, 4, 6
F. 6, 6, 5, 4
G. 3, 7, 9, 2
H. 9, 9, 6, 3
I. 0, 4, 8, 3

Page 17
A. 3 days
B. 9 packages
C. 52 more, 2nd
D. 9 spaces
E. 6 pieces
F. $33

Page 18
A. 3, 3, 6, 7, 5
B. 4, 1, 9, 8, 8
C. 4, 3, 0, 9, 2
D. 9, 9, 6, 1, 7
E. 3, 2, 3, 9, 7
F. 2, 5, 4, 8, 3
G. 6, 8, 5, 2, 2
H. 9, 8, 4, 2, 3
I. 6, 5, 6, 3, 6
J. 4, 3, 9, 9, 8

Page 19
A. 8, 4, 4, 5, 5, 6
B. 6, 4, 9, 2, 4, 9
C. 9, 6, 3, 3, 1, 3
D. 8, 7, 5, 9, 8, 3
E. 3, 2, 9, 6, 4, 7
F. 4, 2, 5, 7, 6, 0
G. 3, 2, 2, 1, 4, 7
H. 6, 2, 9, 6, 7, 5

Page 20
A. 7, 3, 48, 3, 8
B. 3, 36, 6, 2, 0
C. 63, 9, 14, 9, 8
D. 3, 36, 9, 5, 15
E. 18, 4, 6, 4, 9
F. 8, 36, 5, 6, 9
G. 8, 2, 63, 6, 5
H. 15, 3, 48, 12, 9
I. 1, 6, 1, 4, 56
J. 7, 6, 5, 7, 7

Page 21
A. 9, 9, 8, 6, 4, 3
B. 8, 7, 5, 3, 2, 3
C. 5, 9, 1, 6, 8, 3
D. 6, 9, 9, 0, 5, 6
E. 2, 4, 4, 2, 2, 9
F. 7, 7, 6, 2, 2, 9
G. 6, 8, 3, 5, 7, 4
H. 5, 7, 4, 0, 1, 6

Page 22
A. 8, 5, 3, 7, 4
B. 3, 4, 8, 9, 3
C. 4, 9, 0, 1, 2
D. 6, 1, 9, 6, 3
E. 7, 5, 2, 2, 9
F. 1, 7, 8, 1, 5
G. 4, 4, 8, 5, 3
H. 3, 3, 1, 9, 7
I. 4, 6, 2, 4, 8
J. 0, 5, 9, 6, 6

Page 23
A. 20, 24, 25, 45, 24, 0, 15
B. 56, 54, 5, 12, 15, 9, 48
C. 45, 36, 54, 20, 4, 81, 12
D. 36, 12, 24, 63, 8, 45, 6
E. 54, 45, 6, 24, 18, 18, 20
F. 20, 0, 36, 16, 48, 20, 63
G. 18, 16, 54, 63, 36, 14, 15
H. 48, 24, 10, 36, 3, 45, 54

Page 24
A. 1, 6, 3, 3
B. 5, 4, 6, 9
C. 5, 9, 9, 3
D. 4, 6, 2, 8
E. 3, 8, 4, 8
F. 1, 1, 9, 5
G. 3, 0, 5, 8
H. 9, 8, 4, 4
I. 7, 5, 6, 9

Page 25
A. 72 teachers
B. 1 more bag
C. 8 pretzels
D. $49
E. 5 tanks
F. 54 students
   6 teams

Page 26
A. 6, 5, 4, 9, 6
B. 6, 8, 5, 1, 4
C. 9, 5, 4, 2, 4
D. 6, 9, 2, 9, 8
E. 4, 8, 5, 3, 9
F. 6, 4, 9, 6, 7
G. 1, 5, 3, 4, 2
H. 5, 8, 2, 5, 6
I. 9, 2, 3, 0, 3
J. 9, 4, 5, 6, 1

Page 27
A. 9, 5, 9, 6, 2, 4
B. 4, 2, 6, 8, 6, 9
C. 5, 7, 5, 3, 2, 6
D. 4, 9, 3, 7, 0, 9
E. 6, 3, 2, 1, 5, 5
F. 8, 7, 4, 5, 9, 8
G. 4, 5, 8, 5, 9, 6
H. 9, 9, 2, 6, 5, 3

Page 28
A. 5, 0, 24, 3, 8
B. 9, 54, 6, 6, 45
C. 36, 6, 48, 9, 4
D. 3, 56, 5, 4, 54
E. 63, 5, 9, 6, 3
F. 8, 20, 6, 18, 7
G. 6, 2, 10, 1, 4
H. 6, 9, 15, 24, 9
I. 8, 3, 4, 9, 9
J. 3, 3, 9, 20, 5

Page 29
A. 3, 5, 7, 6, 3, 4
B. 3, 2, 7, 5, 9, 4
C. 9, 6, 3, 6, 4, 5
D. 5, 3, 0, 9, 4, 8
E. 5, 1, 3, 6, 6, 8
F. 2, 3, 4, 0, 4, 1
G. 9, 2, 1, 3, 3, 9
H. 8, 9, 5, 9, 5, 5

Page 30
A. 9, 3, 9, 5, 9
B. 8, 9, 9, 4, 4
C. 5, 1, 8, 3, 4
D. 2, 6, 4, 8, 2
E. 4, 7, 9, 8, 2
F. 9, 6, 6, 9, 4
G. 1, 2, 2, 5, 3
H. 5, 6, 5, 2, 9
I. 5, 0, 7, 5, 3
J. 8, 6, 7, 3, 4

Page 31
A. 40, 25, 48, 12, 28, 30, 2
B. 24, 36, 63, 24, 45, 49, 40
C. 36, 8, 24, 12, 64, 8, 30
D. 20, 45, 15, 28, 54, 18, 24
E. 56, 14, 48, 20, 6, 24, 40
F. 30, 12, 0, 45, 40, 24, 28
G. 49, 15, 54, 30, 4, 40, 30
H. 28, 24, 20, 24, 64, 28, 54

Page 32
A. 8, 5, 7, 6
B. 8, 2, 9, 7
C. 8, 9, 4, 8
D. 6, 3, 9, 6
E. 8, 8, 6, 5, 9
F. 6, 7, 7, 6, 5
G. 7, 6, 6, 8
H. 6, 5, 0, 4
I. 3, 5, 4, 8

Page 33
A. No
B. $8
C. 10 sq. ft.
D. 5 seeds
E. 6 plates
F. 7 packs, 15 cards

Page 34
A. 4, 7, 9, 8, 9
B. 6, 5, 5, 6, 5
C. 5, 5, 8, 6, 4
D. 9, 8, 8, 8, 2
E. 4, 5, 4, 7, 5
F. 3, 8, 5, 8, 2
G. 9, 6, 6, 7, 6
H. 8, 0, 3, 4, 6
I. 6, 2, 7, 9, 7
J. 5, 9, 6, 4, 2

Page 35
A. 6, 5, 5, 8, 8, 4
B. 9, 5, 7, 5, 6, 6
C. 8, 4, 9, 4, 8, 7
D. 7, 6, 6, 5, 8, 5
E. 2, 3, 0, 2, 7, 1
F. 7, 9, 6, 4, 3, 8
G. 8, 8, 5, 8, 4, 8
H. 6, 7, 6, 4, 5, 9

Page 36
A. 8, 5, 40, 3, 5
B. 4, 24, 6, 8, 28
C. 12, 7, 49, 9, 6
D. 9, 64, 8, 4, 16
E. 30, 9, 4, 5, 6
F. 2, 28, 1, 6, 5
G. 7, 7, 20, 5, 3
H. 24, 6, 40, 24, 4
I. 8, 5, 5, 4, 30
J. 6, 4, 8, 45, 8

Page 37
A. 8, 5, 2, 6, 3, 7
B. 8, 6, 6, 5, 5, 5
C. 4, 4, 9, 7, 4, 5
D. 5, 7, 3, 9, 8, 8
E. 9, 0, 5, 6, 6, 8
F. 8, 9, 7, 6, 5, 4
G. 6, 3, 4, 6, 3, 4
H. 1, 2, 6, 4, 6, 7

Page 38
A. 6, 8, 3, 6, 0
B. 2, 4, 6, 5, 9
C. 5, 5, 4, 8, 9
D. 6, 5, 1, 2, 7
E. 6, 8, 5, 5, 7
F. 9, 3, 8, 6, 7
G. 4, 9, 2, 8, 8
H. 7, 4, 7, 3, 8
I. 2, 4, 6, 7, 5
J. 7, 1, 9, 5, 6

Page 39
A. 5, 5, 9, 4, 2, 7
B. 6, 4, 7, 8, 3, 1
C. 8, 5, 2, 4, 7, 3
D. 8, 9, 7, 4, 9, 2
E. 6, 3, 2, 7, 5, 4
F. 6, 4, 9, 0, 5, 8
G. 7, 8, 8, 1, 5, 5
H. 6, 7, 9, 8, 4, 6

Page 40
A. 1, 3, 2, 5, 8
B. 3, 6, 7, 4, 6
C. 7, 3, 6, 4, 9
D. 4, 8, 4, 5, 6
E. 7, 9, 9, 7, 5, 3
F. 6, 3, 5, 6, 4, 8
G. 4, 5, 8, 3, 7, 7
H. 7, 8, 5, 7, 6, 4

Page 41
A. 72, 15, 35, 6, 21, 42, 36
B. 16, 27, 32, 32, 30, 40, 81
C. 56, 8, 72, 42, 12, 21, 27
D. 30, 48, 21, 28, 45, 64, 35
E. 24, 32, 63, 7, 24, 54, 21
F. 20, 35, 27, 32, 72, 42, 4
G. 0, 28, 40, 12, 35, 18, 42
H. 24, 49, 18, 72, 20, 27, 24

Page 42
A. 9, 5, 5, 3
B. 7, 3, 9, 2
C. 5, 3, 4, 7
D. 9, 7, 5, 1
E. 3, 6, 6, 5
F. 6, 8, 3, 4
G. 0, 4, 4, 6
H. 3, 4, 9, 7
I. 5, 9, 6, 8

Page 43
A. $8
B. 27 sq. ft.
C. 8 days
D. 48 pieces
E. 6 areas
F. $18

Page 44
A. 9, 6, 6, 7, 3
B. 3, 3, 4, 7, 3
C. 4, 4, 4, 5, 9
D. 4, 8, 9, 5, 4
E. 7, 8, 8, 7, 9
F. 6, 5, 4, 8, 8
G. 1, 4, 7, 4, 7
H. 3, 3, 8, 5, 8

Page 45
A. 3, 4, 5, 6, 9, 7
B. 8, 5, 3, 7, 8, 8
C. 3, 6, 7, 2, 9, 2
D. 9, 5, 7, 6, 3, 8
E. 9, 5, 3, 2, 8, 7
F. 6, 7, 2, 7, 8, 7
G. 4, 6, 9, 8, 4, 5
H. 6, 9, 6, 5, 3, 6

Page 46
A. 2, 4, 35, 7, 4
B. 6, 42, 7, 4, 30
C. 32, 6, 28, 8, 8
D. 3, 36, 8, 6, 21
E. 72, 9, 5, 9, 6
F. 8, 27, 3, 42, 6
G. 4, 9, 64, 8, 5
H. 48, 3, 5, 32, 3

Page 47
A. 8, 3, 5, 9, 8, 3
B. 7, 8, 8, 0, 7, 9
C. 4, 5, 1, 4, 6, 3
D. 7, 9, 7, 8, 7, 3
E. 7, 9, 9, 7, 5, 3
F. 6, 3, 5, 6, 4, 8
G. 4, 5, 8, 3, 7, 7
H. 7, 8, 5, 7, 6, 4

Page 48
A. 9, 5, 1, 5, 9
B. 8, 0, 2, 6, 2
C. 2, 4, 9, 3, 2
D. 7, 4, 6, 5, 4
E. 8, 5, 3, 5, 7
F. 8, 6, 8, 3, 7
G. 3, 5, 4, 4, 3
H. 4, 9, 6, 5, 3
I. 7, 4, 7, 8, 9
J. 4, 7, 7, 2, 7

Page 49
A. 5, 7, 9, 9, 4, 4
B. 3, 6, 8, 6, 7, 4
C. 7, 9, 8, 7, 9, 8
D. 9, 6, 5, 3, 7, 7
E. 8, 4, 5, 7, 3, 5
F. 3, 6, 8, 5, 6, 7
G. 4, 9, 9, 8, 8, 5
H. 7, 4, 8, 9, 3, 7

Page 50
A. 4, 6, 6, 8, 3
B. 5, 3, 4, 4, 7
C. 8, 7, 9, 7, 5
D. 5, 9, 2, 7, 8
E. 7, 3, 7, 5, 9
F. 4, 8, 5, 7, 3
G. 9, 8, 6, 9, 7
H. 3, 7, 8, 7, 6
I. 8, 9, 9, 5, 3
J. 7, 3, 8, 4, 6

Page 51
A. 8, 5, 7, 8, 4, 8
B. 4, 2, 7, 9, 5, 7
C. 3, 6, 9, 8, 1, 4
D. 3, 3, 5, 8, 4, 4
E. 0, 9, 5, 5, 8, 8
F. 9, 2, 7, 3, 7, 9
G. 1, 9, 9, 4, 5, 6
H. 7, 3, 6, 8, 7, 9

Page 52
A. 4 pages
B. 8 stacks, 20 lbs.
C. 7 teams
D. 18 flavors
E. $10 more
F. 2 more tables

Page 53
A. 1, 7, 3, 2, 5, 3
B. 3, 4, 6, 8, 4, 8
C. 9, 7, 4, 7, 4, 5
D. 8, 6, 7, 9, 7, 0
E. 6, 7, 6, 6, 7, 9
F. 7, 6, 4, 8, 6, 9
G. 5, 6, 2, 9, 9, 8
H. 3, 3, 4, 9, 2, 5

Page 54
A. 6, 5, 9, 7, 6
B. 3, 7, 9, 4, 0
C. 5, 7, 2, 5, 9
D. 3, 7, 6, 3, 6
E. 8, 5, 4, 7, 3
F. 3, 9, 7, 8, 8
G. 8, 3, 6, 1, 9
H. 6, 4, 4, 8, 2
I. 7, 9, 4, 7, 9
J. 3, 9, 7, 7, 5

Page 55
A. 7, 8, 8, 1, 6
B. 8, 8, 3, 6, 9, 7
C. 5, 3, 5, 4, 4, 9
D. 7, 6, 3, 5, 9, 2
E. 9, 7, 7, 0, 3, 7
F. 5, 8, 9, 3, 8, 7
G. 7, 5, 4, 2, 9, 3
H. 8, 8, 9, 1, 3, 2

Page 56
A. 9, 5, 7, 7, 6
B. 9, 9, 2, 8, 8
C. 6, 5, 3, 9, 7
D. 8, 7, 1, 7, 4
E. 2, 6, 3, 7, 4
F. 9, 7, 7, 8, 3
G. 4, 0, 8, 3, 3
H. 5, 8, 8, 9, 9
I. 6, 7, 5, 8, 6
J. 5, 5, 4, 7, 9

Page 57
A. 5, 9, 4, 0, 6, 7
B. 7, 9, 4, 7, 4, 5
C. 1, 3, 8, 3, 7, 8
D. 9, 3, 6, 6, 5, 6
E. 4, 2, 1, 3, 9, 4
F. 4, 9, 0, 6, 4, 1
G. 7, 5, 8, 6, 5, 8
H. 2, 1, 3, 5, 4, 8

Page 58
A. 2, 3, 8, 2, 3
B. 8, 4, 8, 7, 5
C. 2, 4, 1, 8, 8
D. 1, 2, 5, 7, 7
E. 4, 3, 5, 0, 8
F. 3, 9, 7, 1, 9
G. 3, 5, 6, 6, 6
H. 2, 5, 9, 8, 4
I. 3, 9, 7, 7, 2
J. 9, 6, 2, 4, 7

Page 59
A. 9, 5, 3, 3, 7, 3
B. 1, 8, 3, 7, 9, 5
C. 6, 8, 0, 5, 2, 5
D. 8, 9, 8, 7, 5, 2
E. 9, 1, 5, 4, 6
F. 7, 7, 9, 2, 9
G. 4, 8, 2, 9, 8
H. 3, 4, 6, 4, 5
I. 8, 4, 1, 9
J. 4, 2, 0, 2, 4

Page 60
A. 7, 9, 3, 2, 7, 6
B. 8, 0, 7, 9, 2, 8
C. 5, 2, 1, 4, 5, 2
D. 7, 4, 2, 8, 8, 9
E. 3, 7, 2, 8, 1
F. 8, 7, 3, 8, 5
G. 6, 5, 3, 9, 6
H. 7, 6, 5, 0, 3
I. 9, 5, 8, 9, 4
J. 6, 3, 1, 7, 6